SCRÍBHINNÍ BÉALOIDIS

FOLKLORE STUDIES

14

UAIR AN CHLOIG COIS TEALLAIGH

Scéalta dá n-inse ag
PÁDRAIG EOGHAIN PHÁDRAIG MAC AN LUAIN
Cruach Mhín an Fheannta, Dún na nGall

SÉAMAS Ó CATHÁIN
a bhailigh, a d'aistrigh agus a chuir nótaí leo

Comhairle Bhéaloideas Éireann
An Coláiste Ollscoile
Baile Átha Cliath
1985

AN HOUR BY THE HEARTH

Stories told by
PÁDRAIG EOGHAIN PHÁDRAIG MAC AN LUAIN
Crooveenananta, Co. Donegal

Collected, translated and annotated by
Séamas Ó Catháin

Comhairle Bhéaloideas Éireann
University College
Dublin
1985

8730

ISBN 0-901120-91-X

Printed in the Republic of Ireland by
The Dundalgan Press, Dundalk
for the publishers
Comhairle Bhéaloideas Éireann
University College
Belfield
Dublin 4

DO HEINRICH WAGNER

CONTENTS

LIST OF ILLUSTRATIONS

Photographs by Lisbeth Östberg.

Pádraig Eoghain Phádraig Mac an Luain

BUÍOCHAS

Tá mé buíoch de Cheann Roinn Bhéaloideas Éireann, An tOllamh Bo Almqvist, Eagarthóir Ginearálta na sraithe seo *Scríbhinní Béaloidis*, as cead a thabhairt domh an t-ábhar seo uilig idir fhuaim agus scríbhinn a fhoilsiú agus as an chomhairle chaoin eolgaiseach a bhronn sé go fial orm le linn domh a bheith ag iarraidh na scéalta seo a chur in ord agus in eagar; ní lú ná sin an chomaoin atá curtha ag Comhairle Bhéaloideas Éireann orm as iad a chur ar fáil don phobal ina dhiaidh sin.

Orthu siad a chuidigh liom ar an iomad bealach agus gur mian liom buíochas ó mo chroí amach a ghabháil leo fosta, tá mo shean-mhúinteoir an tOllamh Heinrich Wagner — is dó siúd a thíolacaim an leabhar seo — agus mo sheanchara an Dr Seosamh Watson, beirt gur éirigh leo mé a choinneáil ón uile chineál dearmad a dhéanamh i ndiaidh dófa an chlóscríbhinn a léamh agus éisteacht leis na scéalta. Rinne beirt bhan uasal de bhunadh na gCruach mórán comhairle den chineál chéanna a chur orm fosta, mar tá Máire Uí Cheallaigh O.S. agus Máire (Rua) Uí Mhaí; chuidigh Pádraig Ó Maí agus Áine Ní Dhíoraí liom chomh maith. Mhol Bríd Mahon athruithe áirithe sa réamhrá agus tá mé buíoch di ar son na comhairle sin. Lisbeth Östberg ón tSualainn a ghlac na grianghrafanna atá i gcló anseo agus gabhaim buíochas ó chroí léi sin agus le Peadar Ó Duibheannaigh a bhronn orm iad. Ba é dianchúram agus saineolas Jackie Small agus Harry Bradshaw a rinne ardchaighdeán fuaime an chaiséid a bhaint amach agus gabhaim buíochas leo siúd, le Máire Diolún agus Anna Germaine gur thit cuid mhaith de obair chrua na clóscríbhneoireachta orthu, le Eddie Buckmaster a tharraing na léarscáileanna, agus le gach aon duine a chuidigh liom an leabhar seo a chur ar fáil. Ní le duine ar bith de na daoine a luaitear anseo nó le duine ar bith eile a bhaineann aon locht nó dearmad de chuid an tsaothair seo ina dhiaidh sin ach liom féin amháin.

Agus an méid sin ráite, thar aon duine nó aon dream eile, tá mé buíoch de Phádraig Eoghain Phádraig Mac an Luain a d'inis na scéalta seo domh, agus dá dhearthráir Conall agus dá dheirfiúr Máire, triúr go raibh sé de phribhléid agam oiread sin oícheanna iontacha chois teallaigh a chaitheamh ina gcuideachta ar na Cruacha. Tá an triúr seo anois ar shlí na fírinne — ar dheis láimh Dé agus i gcomhluadar Phádraig agus Cholm Cille go raibh siad.

SÉAMAS Ó CATHÁIN

Lá Fhéile Pádraig 1985

INTRODUCTION

*Ba mhaith liom, in am ínteacht, cuntas beag a scríobh
fá na Cruacha agus na daoine a casadh orm ann.
Sílim gur sin rud nach dtearnadh agus mar gur
ceantar é nach mbíonn i bhfad ann de réir mo
bharúla, ba mhaith liom tuairisc a fhágáil i mo
dhiaidh go raibh a leithéid ann agus go bhfuil na
daoine ann is deise a casadh riamh orm.* *

"Some time, I would like to write a little account of
the Croaghs and the people I met there. I do not think
this has ever been done and, since, in my opinion,
it is a place that will not survive long, I would wish
to leave after me some tidings of its existence and of
its inhabitants, the nicest people I ever met."

—Seán Ó hEochaidh, Full-time folklore collector

I

In his *Statistical Survey of the County of Donegal* (published in
1802), the author, James McParlan, M.D., has little good to say of
Glenfinn—"The little nook called Glanfyn between the mountains,"
he wrote starkly, "is indeed a wretched country."[1] Of Donegal in
general, at that time, McParlan remarked—"Money and paper are
equally current, except in the mountain region, where I am sorry
to see the degree of ignorance so great, that they totally refuse the
currency of paper being in general quite illiterate."[2] Again, under
the heading "The use of the English language, whether general or
how far encreasing", McParlan observed in his *Survey*—"In the
mountain region the English language is very little known; parents
would wish to instruct their children, but are too poor to pay for any
education for them, in some instances; in many parts there are no

* IFC 1289: 323

schools, and sometimes where they are, the children cannot be spared from working for the potatoe and barley. In the champain parts the English is quite general; the Scotch twang is the vulgar accent of this county."[3]

Through Glenfinn, James McParlan would have penetrated the mountains of Donegal. If that picturesque gateway to the interior of the county would have led him to the very heart of those wild mountains, he would have come to an area that lay somewhat off the beaten track, a place called in Irish *Na Cruacha*, in English, "The Croaghs".[4]

One of the few notices this remote and isolated area gets in tourist literature, or, indeed, in any other literature, occurs in a book called *The Donegal Highlands*, written by the one-time Bishop of Raphoe, the Rev. James McDevitt, D.D., and published in 1866. Heading westwards up Glenfinn and branching off the River Finn and into the Reelan Basin, the author paints the following picture:

> "The direct road leads on to Glenties and affords along its whole length highland scenery, rich and varied as the tourist could desire. Crossing the Reelan bridge, we find ourselves in the midst of the mountains. As we follow up the Reelan river we get at every turn of the road new views of a noble group of steeply-escarped hills, which 'shoulder each other' close on the left. First is Gaugin (1865 feet) conspicuous by its dark colour and isolated summit; then Crovenahanta (1568 feet,) and Lavaghmore (2211 feet,) and Croaghanairigid (Silver Hill,) and other peaks of the Croaghgorm, or Bluestack range peering up behind."[5]

Few travellers, however, took the path to the lonely mountain valley locked away in the shadow of these majestic hills where the stories in this collection were recorded. Even as knowledgeable a native son as Seán Ó hEochaidh, for forty-eight years a full-time folklore collector in Donegal, first with the former Irish Folklore Commission, then until his retirement in 1983, with the Department of Irish Folklore at University College, Dublin, was in total ignorance of the Croaghs for many years. When first despatched there in 1947 by Séamus Ó Duilearga, Honorary Director of the Irish Folklore Commission, he confessed — "Unlike other parts of Donegal, I knew nothing about it, except that it was a remote out-of-the-way place".[6] To Ó hEochaidh's friend and collaborator, Heinrich Wagner, author of the monumental *Linguistic Atlas and Survey of Irish Dialects*, four large tomes based on years of travel and detailed linguistic enquiry all over this island, the Croaghs were, in his own words, "the most inaccessible place I have visited in Ireland."[7] *"Die blauen Bergpyramiden"*, as Wagner called them elsewhere, formed, as he says *"eine Bastion gegen die moderne Zivilisation"*[8] — which is not to say, of course, that the people of the Croaghs were uncivilised, for the mountains that held the English language at bay also held cradled within their embrace a small community of Irish language monoglots who preserved in that tongue one of the richest and purest veins of folk narrative and song tradition in all of Europe.

For nearly three years, Seán Ó hEochaidh, lived and worked among the people of the Croaghs, getting to know them and their traditions better than anyone. He was not stinting in praise of both:

"In my opinion, this is the last real Irish-speaking place in Donegal. Here in these hills they have a civilisation of their own with little or no connection with the outside world. Irish is the language of every family and to call it Irish is no lie, for there is a sweetness and exactness in it that is not found in other places I know. They speak it slowly and distinctly. There are still many people in this area who do not understand a word of English and I know men from this place who, when they go to a fair with a beast, must have recourse to an interpreter to assist them in making the bargain. They buy and sell plenty, nevertheless, and it would be a clever man, indeed, who could make a fool of a man from the Croaghs![9] . . . . The people of the Croaghs are gentle and kind and most welcoming. If a stranger appeared at a house three times the same day, it is their custom to shake hands each time as if they hadn't met for a year. They are just as friendly among themselves as they are to the stranger and are rarely heard to fall out or fight[10] . . . . they are intelligent and sharp-witted and those of them who got a little schooling did well in the places they went to when they left the area. Though they have no 'book learning', they have riches that many men of books do not have — folklore. There are stories, lore, songs, poetry and Fenian tales in them that all belong to the realm of oral literature."[11]

II

It was to the home of a man of the Croaghs, one of these walking repositories of folklore, Pádraig Eoghain Phádraig Mac an Luain,[12] that I made my way for the first time one summer's day in 1962. Seán Ó hEochaidh had come and gone a decade and more before[13] and twenty years before that again, another full-time collector, Liam Mac Meanman of Glenfinn.[14]

The brief sojourns in the Croaghs of Caoimhín Ó Danachair,[15] Séamus Ennis,[16] Simon Coleman[17] and Heinrich Wagner,[18] each intent in his separate way on documenting the traditions of the area, were fading in local memory too. *Sean-Chaìnnt na gCruach* was about to be published and it may be that this fact was brought to my attention as an undergraduate at Queen's University Belfast by its co-author and my teacher, Heinrich Wagner, thus re-awakening my interest in the Croaghs. This interest was first fostered by the great Rannafast storyteller, Micí Sheáin Néill Ó Baoill[19] in whose house I stayed as a schoolboy learning Irish and at whose hearth, like many another student at the local Irish College, I got my first taste of the old Donegal storytelling tradition in full bloom. Micí talked enthusiastically about the Croaghs, the purity of the Irish and the old-fashioned way of life he observed there. Years later, I was to bring him back to the Croaghs to meet the man whose stories and store of tradition I had begun to record there,[20] but it was long before that, during the long summer vacation of 1962, that, with two companions, I set up camp in Pat Gibbons' "garden" in the townland of Dergroagh at the foot of Gaugin mountain.

Pat, like every inhabitant of those parts, was steeped in tradition and over the years, I managed to record many bits and pieces from him.[21] It was to Pádraig Eoghain Phádraig, however, that he directed my footsteps for stories and so it was that I tramped westwards to Crooveenananta to find Pádraig busy cleaning out the byre. Without much ceremony, I asked him would he tell me a story and though the moment could not have been more inopportune and, just then, nothing further from his mind than storytelling, after a few futile attempts to get rid of me, Pádraig downed tools, ordered his sister, Máire, to make tea and seated by the little table that swung on hinges from the wall (and was hoisted again when all was over),

Pádraig told a version of the story here simply called *"Goll Mac Morna"* (No. 21). Story told, and tea drunk, Pádraig promptly returned to his work and I made my way down the valley and back across the Reelan river to Dergroagh.

As I discovered later, Pádraig's reputation in the area for irascibility was second to none and Pat Gibbons who had looked forward (mischievously, I think) to hearing about my reception by the man who was said not to suffer fools gladly was both disappointed and delighted at my success. I do not recall ever receiving the sharp edge of Pádraig's tongue, but I often heard him rebuke his younger brother Conall during recording sessions for what he considered an unwarranted interjection — the offering of a clue to a half-remembered song, for example, the words of which had momentarily escaped Pádraig. *"Níl gar don bheirt againn a bheith ag dul ann"* he would snap at Conall — "There's no point in both of us going into it" (i.e. the tape recorder). Pádraig took the business of recording very seriously, indeed, and looked forward to my visits greatly as, indeed, did his brother Conall and his sister, Máire. On my arrival, after the initial exchanges and small talk and following his customary enquiry about the state of things in the North (*"Caidé mar tá na Gaeil ins na Sé Chontae?"*), Pádraig would always ask — *"An bhfuil an ceamara leat an iarraidh seo?"* ("Do you have the camera [i.e. the tape recorder] with you this time?") With that, the folklore would begin to flow and thenceforth songs and stories held sway by that fireside.

Once, Pádraig pulled my leg about my own seemingly too anxious dedication to my task. Just as we were about to commence one of our sessions, he innocently enquired why I wanted to bother recording all this material anyway. I muttered something about posterity and how fine it would be for those who followed after us to hear his stories which would otherwise be lost forever. But, what was the point, said Pádraig, hadn't I heard that the world was only supposed to last 2,000 years from the time of Our Lord and wasn't the date almost up already? I was stumped, but Pádraig having had a bit of fun at my expense quickly let me off the hook by declaring that there was a little addendum to the story and that the time span specified was actually 2,000 years and a bit . . . and nobody could tell how long the bit might be!

III

According to Pádraig, the house in which he and Conall and Máire dwelt was the first house to be built in the Croaghs. The family name of McLoone together with McHugh dominates the district. In my time there, there was also a scattering of other names including Gibbons, Given, Gallagher, McDermott, McGinley, Quinn, Timoney and Ward strung out along the valley, but everywhere one went there were McLoones, who spoke Irish with their own peculiar family intonation, a kind of drawl that singled them out from the rest of the inhabitants. Among the McLoones, there was also a strong family tradition that the first people to settle in the Croaghs came from neighbouring Tyrone, only a short distance away, as the crow flies, across the mountains and over the gap of Barnesmore. Indeed, the names McLoone (usually spelled McAloon in Tyrone) and McHugh are still quite frequently met with in West Tyrone and intercourse between the Croaghs and Aghyaran and Castlederg on the Tyrone side of the border was lively enough until fairly recent times, despite the mountain barrier that lies between them.[22] Ó hEochaidh and Wagner are probably right in their assertion that this valley was settled no more than a few hundred years ago, perhaps in Penal Times. This judgement is based on the apparent lack of archaeological remains, the minimal utilization of peat bogs, the existence of close-knit and closely related family groups and, of course, the persistent lively memory of an outside origin for these self-same families.[23] Our storyteller, Pádraig Eoghain Phádraig Mac an Luain, takes the latter tradition a stage farther than most in proposing an outside origin with Spanish connections for himself and his people:

"This is the first house to be built in the Croaghs, the house we're in now. There was a man of the McLoones lived in it and almost four generations have lived in it now. They were soldiers that came from Spain — two soldiers called McLoone that came from Spain — and one of them came here and I don't know where the other went, back to the lower part of Boylagh, I think. And the McLoones are still there too and in this place as well. And that's all I can say about them. I heard it from my father, I did."[24]

Whatever about the origins of the refugees who, according to tradition, first populated the Croaghs and whatever about Pádraig Eoghain Phádraig's claims concerning the family homestead, the house of *Bunadh Eoghain Phádraig*, as that branch of the McLoones was called,[25] was certainly built in the old style. A long, low (originally) thatched house, it had a gigantic chimney fitted against the inside gable end and extending down into the house with an out-shot bed ranged comfortably alongside it and the open-hearth fire. Opposite the chimney and hearth, a short flight of stairs ran steeply up to an enclosed half-loft. To the left of the stairs and between it and the half-door, stood the dresser, while a door on the other side of the stairs led off down to the lower room and the sleeping quarters. On the wall opposite the half-door, a tiny window with an enormous sill, the full thickness of the wall in which it was recessed, shed a thin shaft of light out across the flag-stoned floor. A small enamel alarm clock, often with its face turned to the wall and which never seemed to be wound, sat unnoticed on the sloping whitewashed sill. Beside the window-opening, a lamp hung on the wall and across the kitchen on the opposite wall beside the door and suspended high above it hung an array of walking-sticks and ornamental shepherd's crooks. A bench along the wall and a few chairs scattered here and there around the floor provided all the seating accommodation apart from Pádraig's seat of honour by the fire, in the corner opposite the out-shot bed. This was an old seat salvaged from a car and seated low on its springy cushion, close to the floor, Pádraig would stretch his feet out towards the fire, so near at times, that I thought his *giosáin* or knitted woollen socks must surely catch fire. It was Conall's job to keep the fire going and ferry in the fuel in creelfulls from the mountain. On a winter's night, more often than not he would empty the full of a creel of turf on the fire. Later, Máire would make the tea, skilfully positioning the teapot to draw on the hot embers round the edge of this veritable furnace, with a couple of duck eggs bubbling alongside in a soot-blackened "pandy". A pair of collie dogs and, in the lambing season, a motherless lamb or two staring out from upturned creels shared the frugal comfort of the kitchen with its human inhabitants.

IV

From the time of that first visit in 1962, I was a constant, if somewhat irregular visitor to *Teach Eoghain Phádraig*. Apart from a five-month spell of residence in the Croaghs in the autumn and winter of 1964-5,[26] my opportunities for calling there were limited. All of the material presented here, for example, was recorded during forays northwards to Donegal from University College Galway where I lectured in Modern Irish from 1970-4. On my visits to the McLoone household, I was sometimes accompanied by friends and relations from Tyrone, other parts of Ireland and, even on a number of occasions by visitors from abroad.[27] Irish-speaking visitors were particularly welcome since neither Pádraig nor Máire could speak English and only Conall could manage to conduct some kind of conversation in that language.

Pádraig was already out of his teens when the first school opened in the Croaghs in 1907[28] and when, as a young man, he became a hired farm-hand, it was with an Irish-speaking family near the Croaghs, thus presenting him with little opportunity to learn the English language.[29] He told me that he had learned some English once, but that he had long since forgotten it, thus surely making him one of the few people to have managed such a feat in 20th century Ireland. His style of Irish, as also his storytelling style, is simple and direct. The fact that his speech, and the speech of other monoglot Irish speakers in this locality was liberally sprinkled with English loan-words, some instances of which occur in the stories presented here, is a phenomenon in its own right and one worthy of closer examination and study. Suffice it to say here that some of these loan-words arrived in the Croaghs with new technology and kindred developments giving rise to such examples as "camera", "forestry" (p. 8) and "wire" (p. 25) ; others like "heat" (in the sense of "time", "occasion"), "bit" (p. 11) and "weapon" (three favourite and frequently employed words in the Croaghs) belong to an older stratum of loan-words and the use of "big man" (p. 40) for *"fear mór"* or words like "start" (p. 5) and "extra" (p. 16) may, perhaps, be excused on the grounds that they gave legitimate expression to a desire for choice and variety in speech for artistic purposes. The pressure that monoglot Irish-speakers such as Pádraig Eoghain Phádraig may have felt as a result of finding themselves in such a minority in their own country, may also have served to encourage them to employ, in however disjointed fashion, whatever little English they happened to know, by way of showing off even individual words and phrases and of demonstrating that their ignorance of that language was not, in fact, total. For all that, the volume and frequency of loan-words encountered in this context is both surprising and disappointing, all the more so since they seem to have spilled so readily from the mouths of such excellent Irish-speakers as our storyteller.[30] At the same time, it is important to note that the communities of Irish-speakers along the banks of the Finn and Reelan rivers still held the Irish spoken in the Croaghs in high esteem, even going so far as to maintain that, unlike them, the Croaghs people did *not* mix English loan-words through their Irish speech.[31] "*Tá sean-Ghaeilge mhaith fá na Cruacha*" ("The Croaghs has the real old Irish") was their customary accolade of approbration and recognition of a dimension of excellence and authenticity that, in spite of everything, was undeniably part and parcel of "*Gaeilge na gCruach*".

All the recordings presented here were made by me at Pádraig Eoghain Phádraig's own fireside in Crooveenananta. Present on all occasions were his brother Conall and his sister Máire whose voices intrude briefly on tracks 6, 9 and 15. Generally, Conall and Máire just sat and listened with great attention to Pádraig who always dominated the proceedings. Máire, especially, kept in the background, only addressing me directly when inviting me to sit over to the table and enjoy the food which she had prepared for me. When I had it, I always offered Máire a drop of whiskey which she generally accepted, taking a small glass from the dresser, wiping it and gently placing it on the table beside me. I would fill the glass and Máire would return from the far end of the kitchen to reclaim it and then drink it down at the dresser with her back turned to me. When pressed, she would accept a second drink, this time placing her empty glass on the very corner of the table before retreating once again. Once emptied this time, the glass was wiped and replaced on the dresser and Máire's drinking was over and done with for that occasion. Pádraig and Conall were equally sparing in their use of alcohol, but my gesture in occasionally offering them a drink was always accepted and now and then reciprocated with a bottle or two of stout which they sometimes had in the house.

Máire's diligence in providing tea for her visitors often posed problems for me in my efforts to make reasonably interference-free sound-recordings, especially when she set about washing up the dishes afterwards, just when her brother Pádraig would be getting into good humour for talking. The rattle of dishes in a tin basin placed on the table just behind me threatened to play havoc with my plans and only the intervention of my wife (whose company was much appreciated by Máire since female visitors to the house were few and far between) with an offer of assistance would lead to the swift completion of this chore and then leave me only the Tilley lamp which which to contend. It hissed and spluttered on the wall behind where Pádraig lounged on his car seat, the noise it made gradually fading to a less objectionable level as the shadows from the fire lengthened and flickered until, maddeningly, Conall would leap forward, give the Tilley a thorough good pumping and set it hissing and spluttering as bad as ever again. Other background noises which mark the tapes I filled as field-recordings were more acceptable, perhaps: the growl of a dog, the quacking of a duck, the clucking of a hen perched on the half-door or, as in Nos. 12, 13, 14 and 15, the bleating of a lamb caged in an upturned creel on the kitchen floor. The ticking of the clock posed no problem as it sat silent in the house where time stood still and three nonagenerians lived life as if it would go on forever.

The collection of folklore material I made from Pádraig (and on occasions, from his brother, Conall) covers the period 1964-1979. All of my early recordings, made in the mid-1960s and consisting entirely of the words of songs, have been transcribed. Most of my material from the early 1970s has also been transcribed, but there is a substantial residue from my last years working with Pádraig which remains untranscribed and has not been indexed in any form. All in all, about twelve hours of tape recordings made by me in the Croaghs, the vast bulk of it taken down from Pádraig Eoghain Phádraig, are deposited in the sound archives of the Department of Irish Folklore at University College Dublin. This material covers a wide area ranging from custom and belief, proverbs and sayings, riddles and prayers, folktales and Fenian tales to rhymes, *cante fables* and songs.

"Wording" songs was a great pastime of Pádraig's and, indeed, of other noted Croaghs tradition-bearers too.[32] Unlike his father,

Eoghan Phádraig Mac an Luain, Pádraig was no singer, but his interest in the old songs was no less intense for all that. Once when I asked him where he learned the words of some song or other, he replied: "The man that was here had that song. Ah, what song didn't he have! He surely had every song and he could sing too."[33]

Pádraig described for me how his father and his uncle once sang their hearts out at a Harvest Fair in the town of Glenties with a circle of rapt admirers gathered round them and on the table in front of them, that was loaded down with drinks which had been bought for them, not as much space as you could lay a finger on. Later, the Glen of Glenties would ring to the sound of their voices as they made their way home, up through Silver Hill, over the *Stocán* and down home to Crooveenananta, where, said Pádraig, his father might stand with his back to the fire and sing three songs in a row before drawing breath. *"Bhí sé chomh binn leis an chuach."* ("He was as sweet as the cuckoo"), Pádraig used to say. Among the songs which I recorded from Pádraig, all of which he got from his father, were: *An Cailín Rua, Thall ag Tigh an Óil, Seachrán Chairn tSiail, Buachaill ón Éirne, Siubhán Ní Dhuibhir, An Seanduine Dóite, Gasúr an Bhéarla, Túirne Mháire, Na Gamhna Geala, Dónall Óg, A Sheanbhean Aosta, Gráinne na gCuirnín, Chuaigh mé 'na Rosann ar Cuairt* and *Casadh an tSúgáin.* Well aware of his shortcomings as a singer, Pádraig had the humility to ask: *"An ndéarfaidh mé ina chainteanna nó ina seort ceoil é—cé acu?"* ("Will I 'word' it or sing it after a fashion—which?"). Having delivered himself of ten or eleven verses of a song, and keen and complete though his memory generally was, he might occasionally find himself having to confess—*"Ach bhí ceathrú eile ann agus ní thig liom theacht uirthi!"* ("There was another verse to it, but I can't recall it!").

For Pádraig, the words were all important and not just because he was totally incapable of putting an air to them either. I saw this most powerfully demonstrated one evening I played an archive recording of Anna Nic an Luain[34] for him. He and Máire and Conall solemnly listened to Anna's voice from beyond the grave, intoning the words of some old song, and without the slightest trace of nostalgia, Pádraig noted critically when all was over—*"D'fhág sí ceathrú amháin amuigh!"* ("She left out a verse!").

Eight lines that escaped his own long memory were those which went to make up two of the four verses of the song said to have been composed by the human husband of the mermaid — a man of the Gallaghers — in mourning for the wife he lost on her return to the sea whence she originally came (No. 15, p. 28). Pádraig's father, Eoghan, knew this song and had given it in its entirety, along with many other songs, to Seosamh Laoide[35] (or "Lloyd", as Pádraig called him) during a week-long visit to Donegal town, a visit remembered by Pádraig like this — "He spent a week in Donegal town with a man they called Lloyd. He was there for a week one Christmas, singing, and he gave all his songs to Lloyd."[36]

Whatever number of songs may have been recorded by "Lloyd" from Eoghan Mac an Luain on that occasion, only one of them, to the best of my knowledge, ever appeared in print. On my next visit to Crooveenananta, I had with me a copy of the book in which it appeared[37] and from it I read aloud the two missing verses. Our roles reversed that evening the collector become informant, as Pádraig valiantly attempted to fix the words in his memory, I was called upon to repeat those lost lines over and over again.

On another occasion, together with some friends, I arrived in Crooveenananta to find Conall and Pádraig busy making hay in a small field behind the house. Pádraig was building the hay cocks and Conall was raking in the hay and they were both making heavy weather of it all. Our arrival amounted to nothing less than the creation of an instant *meitheal* and we soon made short work of raking in the hay and, before long, Pádraig had built a number of cocks and the work was done. When the last rope was tied, Pádraig, delighted with the speedy completion, leaned on his rake in the middle of the field and gave us a spontaneous rendition of *Casadh an tSúgáin*.

Pádraig's voice is also to be heard among the recordings from the Croaghs made in 1948 by Caoimhín Ó Danachair.[38] As far as I know, no other recordings of him exist apart from those made by me and by RTÉ.

He was known to Seán Ó hEochaidh, of course, whose folklore manuscripts contain a number of items taken down from him; Ó hEochaidh's Croaghs diary for 25.2.1948 reads — ". . . I returned to the Croaghs and I worked till midnight with Seán Mac an Bháird, Micheál Mac an Luain agus Pádraig Mac an Luain."[39] In a passage illustrating something very reminiscent of Pádraig's short-tempered reaction to his brother's attempts to jog his memory, Liam Mac Meanman notes in his diary for 5.2.1936 — "Micheál Mac an Luain was thinking of a story and Pádraig Mac an Luain was helping him and Micheál told him to stop, that he was only confusing him. He couldn't think of the story when the others present were talking and they had to stop."[40] Liam Mac Meanman's diary for the following day (6.2.1936) notes — "There was a man here last night, Micheál Mac an Luain. He has long Fenian tales but he wasn't able to record them on the machine because there were too many people there. He is somewhat shy but he is willing to give them to me. There was another man there who didn't have the courage to record either. His father, Eoghan Phádraig Mac an Luain was outstanding for Irish songs."[41]

VI

Nearly thirty years after Seán Ó hEochaidh's spell as a collector in the Croaghs, he returned there with me for the making of a television film illustrating his work in the field. When they met, Pádraig Eoghain Phádraig greeted Seán with the customary friendly handshake and then, eyeing him up and down, declared in his usual forthright manner — "*A Sheáin Uí Eochaidh, tá tú in do sheanduine liath!*" ("Seán Ó hEochaidh, you're a grey old man!").

To his own impending death, he adopted the same unsentimental approach. When Máire died, she left her two brothers desolate. They never ceased to mourn her passing, always making the point to visitors that they managed but poorly without her and recalling how well, in her simple way, she provided for all who crossed her threshold. Pádraig was not to follow her yet, but I think it is true to say that when she departed, he lost his will to live. In May 1977, less than a year after her death, I arrived in the Croaghs accompanied by Seán Ó hEochaidh and a crew from RTÉ headed by TV Producer, Joe Mulholland. We were engaged in documenting the work done by Seán in various parts of Donegal during his long career and Pádraig Eoghain Phádraig was to be one of the four singers and storytellers destined to feature in that programme.[42] I approached the house, which seemed deserted, to discover Pádraig alone, lying in the out-shot bed, beside a smouldering fire struggling for life on the hearth. *"Tá an bás agam."*[43] ("I am dying."), he replied in a matter-of-fact way to my enquiry after his health. I got the impression that though he would have cheerfully passed away there and then, his time had not yet come. When I asked, if, in spite of his feeling so poorly, he might oblige me with a story or two for the benefit of the film-unit poised for action outside, he agreed to do so without any hesitation. A moment or two later, Conall who had been shepherding his flock on the hills, returned and soon there was a roaring fire on the hearth and, in a house which knew no newspapers, radio or television, in the glare of spotlights and in front of a kitchen-full of strangers, most of whom understood only very little of what he was saying, Pádraig was performing as good as ever.[44]

It would not have been easy to avoid coming in contact with the tradition in a place like the Croaghs where everyone had a story to tell and where folk song and many varieties of folk narrative were rampant.[45] One of the very best of Seán Ó hEochaidh's Croaghs informants in the 1940s was Peadar Ó Tiománaí, a man named by Pádraig Eoghain Pádraig as being the source for many of his shorter pieces and anecdotes. Of Peadar Ó Tiománaí, Seán Ó hEochaidh wrote:

> As I often say of Peadar, there's not a word comes out of his mouth but should be written down. He's as full of words as any man I ever met and it's in his nature, by all accounts . . . I conversed for a while and it wasn't long till Peadar's diction set me writing. He went from one bit to the next and to make a long story short, it was eleven o'clock before I left him. I was delighted I had come to see him. As usual, he didn't think it was worthwhile writing down his *seanchas* at all; instead of that, however, it was more important than many of the folktales common in the place. Peadar knew all the proverbs, sayings, customs and beliefs of the place and it was a great pleasure to work with him . . . Peadar is a man who knows hardly any folktales, but as to *seanchas* it would be hard to find his equal. Another thing too — in his ordinary conversation, he uses nothing but idioms. I don't believe I have met anyone as eloquent as him in all my travels. He's

a real *scalladóir*[46] as they say of him in the Croaghs. Of course, it's in his nature and comes as easily to him as swimming does to a duck. All his people were like that and no wonder, for they were descended from poets. Peadar's relationship to Tadhg of the Women — a poet of the place long ago — isn't all that far removed.[47]

Pádraig Eoghain Phádraig, as I say, drew heavily (though not exclusively) on Peadar Ó Tiománaí as a source of traditional information of one kind and another, but, especially, for the kind of stories represented by Nos. 1-17 in this collection and Seán Ó hEochaidh's description of *his* informant, Peadar Ó Tiománaí reminds me very much of *mine*, Pádraig Eoghain Phádraig Mac an Luain. These snippets of *seanchas* — for they were regarded as little more than snippets by men like these — were just as likely to be thrown up in the course of what they might regard as being a fairly ordinary conversation as to be the result of diligent ferreting by skilled collectors. *Seanchas* like this formed part of the natural flow of talk and entertainment around the fireside as is evidenced where audience participation is audible in these recordings (Texts 12, 13, 14, 15, 18, 21 and 22 for example).[48] They are short and satisfying to both teller and listener alike. For two pieces of *Fiannaíocht* Nos. 21 and 22 are also remarkably compact. By comparison, the longer items here (Nos. 18, 19 and 20) lack some of this polish though they are none the less authentic and enjoyable for all that.[49] They seemed to take their place less easily by that fireside, though they were still told with great gusto (especially No. 20).

VII

In his article *"Tomhaiseanna ó Thír Chonaill"*,[50] Seán Ó hEochaidh describes how he once stole a glance in through Anna Nic an Luain's doorway to find Anna rattling off riddles and posers to a bunch of children gathered round her feet. Pádraig and Conall also enjoyed testing me out with riddles and reciting (nonsense) rhymes.[51] Once Pádraig tried me with something he called *"Cleas na bPréataí"* — a kind of "Spot the Lady" — with spuds. This is how he described it:

"Well, that trick on the floor, you saw it yourself. You had it as soon as it was done. I still had a potato in the cap and I'd leave it with the other one till I had four of them gathered together. You'd put down four on the floor, first of all—the four of them spaced out from one another. And I'd still have one with me in the cap. And I'd always leave the cap in which I had the potato in the place I was lifting the potatoes. And I'd gather the four together with it in that way. And I'd have them with me in the cap every time I left them. 'Over by the river, back along the river, may you not "buy benefit" unless you do what I ask'—you would say that each time. That was only a kind of patter, you know."[52]

From time to time, that same flag-stoned floor resounded to the noise of dancing feet when Conall—known to one and all as "*Conall an Damhsa*" ("Dancing Conall")—would consent to show off some of his fancy steps. All he needed was a bit of music and very little persuasion. He made valiant efforts to play the fiddle too, but his talent lay in his feet not in his fingers. Members of the famous Donegal fiddling family—the Dohertys (Micí and John), or "the Simeys" as they were more commonly called—were frequent visitors to the Croaghs and welcome guests there and aspiring musicians of the locality (including Conall) never missed a chance to listen and learn from them.[53] Once I saw the kitchen filled with dancers when, some time during the winter of 1965, one of the McLoone brothers—Peadar, I think—returned with his wife on a visit home from America.[54] There was "open house" in *Teach Eoghain Phádraig* that evening, a kind of "convoy"[55] in reverse, as the rafters rang to the lilt of the "Highlands" and "Mazurkas" so popular in those parts and Conall danced his party pieces.

In time, only Conall would remain to tread those same flagstones, for Máire passed away in 1977 and Pádraig died in 1979.[56] Shortly after, Conall went to live with his sister Brigid in nearby Silver Hill and silence fell forever on yet another fireside of the Croaghs. May they all rest in peace. The sound of their Gaelic voices lives again in these recordings and may now be heard once again to echo far and wide in this *Uair an Chloig Cois Teallaigh* from the Croaghs.

VIII

The notes on the folklore contents of these stories are intended to provide the reader with background information about them, particularly in their national and, where applicable, their international context. References are provided to a selected range of comparative material in manuscript and printed sources. The titles of each of the twenty-two items printed here have been provided by me.

The notes on the Irish spoken by Pádraig Eoghain Phádraig Mac an Luain in these recordings are mainly aimed at calling attention to various aspects of this dialect of Irish which, as Wagner indicates in his introduction to *SCC*, is the same as that described by E.C. Quiggin in his *A Dialect of Donegal (DD)*. Hitherto, apart from the relatively small amount of material published in *LASID* 1 and 4 and in *SCC*, very little of value for the study of Croaghs Irish has become available. The recordings and texts presented here supply, on the one hand, evidence of a number of interesting deviations from the dialect described in *DD* and, on the other, demonstrate connections and associations with dialects of Irish formerly spoken in other parts of Donegal and in Tyrone.

The recordings — all of which were made in the McLoone family home in Crooveenananta — speak for themselves; the written word which accompanies them highlights the many discrepancies which exist between pronunciation and spelling, showing, in many respects, the reconciliation of Ulster Irish to the demands of standard Irish as outlined in *An Caighdeán Oifigiúil*,[57] to be a matter of real difficulty, to say the very least. Nevertheless, in the interest of uniformity and readability, it has been felt necessary to apply here a system of spelling which adheres as closely as possible to the official standard, while, at the same time, making every effort to adequately represent the Irish dialect of the Croaghs, especially in matters relating to morphology and syntax. Some minor alterations to the spelling of quotations from IFC[58] manuscript sources in the introduction and notes, bringing it in to line with modern usage, have also been made.

Occasional gaps in the texts, indicated by three dots (. . .), represent longer breaks in the recordings as they were made in the field; similarly, absent individual words are supplied here and there in the texts within square brackets. Various questions and interpolations by me (*SÓC*) and other remarks made by Conall Eoghain Phádraig (*CEP*) have been transcribed, though Máire Eoghain Phádraig's background commentary to Text No. 9 has not. Pádraig Eoghain Phádraig has been abbreviated as *PEP*.

1. *Statistical survey of the County of Donegal with observations on the means of improvement; drawn up in the year 1801, for the consideration, and under the direction of The Dublin Society.* By James McParlan, M.D. (Dublin 1802), 34.

2. *Ibid.* 82.

3. *Ibid.* 101. John Braidwood, in his essay "Ulster and Elizabethan English", published in *Ulster Dialects* (Belfast 1964), comments (p. 35) — "If the Donegal Irish had no English they were accustomed to say that they had no Scots . . . At the beginning of this century Donegal Irish engaged themselves as farm servants in the Laggan district and spoke of 'going up till the Lagan to lift the Scotch,' i.e. to learn English."

4. "In the south-eastern corner of the Parish of Inniskeel lies an isolated lonely glen in the shadow of the Blue Stacks. The entire glen is about five miles in length. The little Reelan river runs down through the middle of it and north of the glen lies the famous *Bealach na gCreach*. Along the banks of this river, there are seven townlands — Silver Hill (one of the best-named townlands in Ireland, according to tradition), Croaghubbrid, Doocrow, Lacroagh, Crooveenananta, Meenasrone and Clogher." (My translation from the Irish of Seán Ó hEochaidh in *Sean-Chainnt na gCruach* [*SCC*]). The exact location of the places named here as well as a discussion of these and other placenames of the locality can be found in my "Placenames of Inniskeel and Kilteevoge" (*PIK*).

5. James McDevitt, *The Donegal Highlands* (Dublin 1866), 210.

6. "*Seach ceantar ar bith eile i dTír Chonaill, ní raibh eolas dá laghad agam air, ach amháin go bhfuil fhios agam gur áit iargcúlta chúilriascúil é* " (IFC 1289:75). Seán Ó hEochaidh's diary, in which he recorded some of his experiences in the Croaghs, is contained in this volume and runs from 5.5.1947 until 10.4.1948. His introductory essays in *SCC* "Na Cruacha i dTír Chonaill" and "Croidhe na Féile" give an accurate reflection of the sort of material contained in this diary.

7. H. Wagner, *Linguistic Atlas and Survey of Irish Dialects* (*LASID*), Vol. 1 (Dublin 1958), p. xv. The Croaghs is Point 83 in Wagner's *Atlas*; his informants for the material contained in *LASID* 1 — Séamus Mac Aoidh and Máire Nic Luain — were drawn from the two most significant families in the area (cf. p. xviii). Further dialect material from the Croaghs can be found in *LASID* 4 (Dublin 1969), p. 134-46.

8. My translation from the Irish of Seán Ó hEochaidh in *SCC*, 2.

9. *Ibid.* 13-4.

10. *Ibid.* 13.

11. *Ibid.* 12.

12. *anglice* Patrick McLoone (born 14.9.1885, died 8.2.1979).

13. He conducted almost two year's intensive fieldwork in this area in the late 1940s, subsequently paying only sporadic visits there.

14. Liam Mac Meanman was a full-time collector in Donegal from 9.9.1935 until 31.8.1937. His folklore manuscripts contain a sizeable amount of valuable material from the Croaghs, although, according to his diary, he only made two short stays there (3.2.1936-8.2.1936 [IFC 295:58-84] and 12.4.1937-17.4.1937 [IFC 420:81-91]).

15. Ó Danachair's concern here was to assist in recording on gramophone discs the best of the informants whom Ó hEochaidh had unearthed during his stay in the Croaghs. A van (which I heard referred to in the Croaghs as "*an* tank *mór* ["the big tank"]) equipped with battery-driven disc-cutting apparatus was used for this purpose. An account of Ó Danachair's activities in this context on behalf of the Irish Folklore Commission is given by him in "Sound recording of Folk Narration in Ireland in the late Nineteen Forties", *Fabula* 22 (1981), p. 312-5.

16. It does not appear that Ennis visited the Croaghs during his period of service with the Irish Folklore Commission (1.6.1942-1.8.1947) though this omission was later made good according to Seán Ó hEochaidh and as witnessed by the vivid memories of his singing and piping still alive in that area.

17. In the course of a short visit to Donegal, while briefly in the employ of the Irish Folklore Commission, Simon Coleman R.H.A. spent three days drawing and painting in the Croaghs. He was accompanied by Seán Ó hEochaidh. His impressions of the people and the place, as well as an account of the work he did there, can be found in IFC 1615: 21-35 (his diary).

18. Cf. Note 7 *supra*. An account of Wagner's visit to the Croaghs (13.10.1947 − 17.10.1947) is given by Seán Ó hEochaidh in his diary for those dates (IFC 1289: 285-94). Proinsias Ó Conluain of Radio Éireann and Canon Coslett Ó Cuinn (cf. IFC 420:84) also collected in this area.

19. For a collection of his stories in print, cf. *Maith Thú, a Mhicí* (ed. an tAth. Seosamh Maguidhir [Béal Feirste 1956]) and on gramophone record cf. *Scéalta Aduaidh* (Gael-Linn EEF 7 [Baile Átha Cliath 1959]). The IFC manuscript collection of material taken down from this storyteller, mainly by Seán Ó hEochaidh, runs to nearly 1,400 pages.

20. Pádraig Eoghain Phádraig and Micí Sheáin Néill swapped stories on that occasion — "*an fear a bhfuil an Ghaeilge aige*" ("the man who knows Irish") was how Pádraig later referred to him (cf. Tape 84/1 SÓC [28.12.1974]).

21. Cf. S. Ó Catháin, "Ar na Cruacha agus·ar an Lagán", *Sinsear* (1982-3), p. 91-9.

22. *Ibid.* Two Irish-speakers from West Tyrone feature on the Doegen records made in 1929 (cf. RIA Minutes 1931-2). The texts of these recordings appear in *LASID* 4 (1969), p. 292-4 (Appendix 2 by Colm Ó Baoill). The speakers were Pádraig Ó Gallchobhair, Tullynashane, Killeter, and Máire McDaid, Fourth Corgary, Aghyaran. *"Droichead an Chró"* (The Croagh Bridge), an unofficial border crossing between Tyrone and Donegal, near Barnesmore, and *"Aonach na Deirge"* (Castlederg Fair) mark the usage of two Tyrone placenames in the Irish of the Croaghs. G. B. Adams, in the introduction to *Ulster Dialects* notes among the special features of the English dialect of that part of Tyrone—"an intonation pattern which is quite distinct from that of other [Ulster] dialects." The similarity between this intonation pattern, as it still exists in Tyrone English and as it can be heard in various recordings of the dialect of Irish once spoken in Tyrone, and the intonation pattern of the Irish spoken by members of the McLoone families of the Croaghs is quite striking.

23. *SCC* 10.

24. *"Seo an chéad teach a* build*áileadh ar na Cruacha, an teach a bhfuil muid ann. Bhí fear de Chlainn 'ic a' Luain ina chónaí ann agus tá ceithre* genera-tion *caite anois ann. Saighdiúirí a bhí ann a tháinig as an Spáinn—dhá shaighdiúir de Chlainn 'ic a' Luain a tháinig as an Spáinn agus tháinig fear acu chun an bhaile seo agus níl fhios agamsa cá háit a dteachaidh an fear eile—siar go híochtar Baiollach, sílim, a chuaigh sé. Tá Clainn 'ic a' Luain thiar fosta ar fad agus ar an bhaile seo. Chuala mé ag m'athair é, chuala"* (Tape 85/1 SÓC [26.12.1973]).

25. Other branches of the family were known as *Bunadh Eoghain Mhicheáil* and *Bunadh Eoghain Sheáin*.

26. While I was collecting material for my M.A. thesis on the placenames of Inniskeel and Kilteevoge (*PIK*).

27. Including Lisbeth Östberg from Sweden who took all the photographs published here. She and Conall also exchanged tunes on the fiddle on that occasion.

28. *SCC* 3, 12.

29. In his diary for 5.2.1936 (IFC 295:71), Liam Mac Meanman observes: *"Nuair a bhí na seandaoine seo óg, ní raibh duine ar bith ag dul chun na scoile nó iomrá air. Deir na seandaoine nach bhfuair siad seans an Béarla a bheith acu—iad gan scoil"* ("When these old people were young, there was no one going to school or even thinking of it. There was no school in the Croaghs at the time. The old people say that being left without a school is what left them without any chance of learning English.").

30. Énrí Ó Muirgheasa railed against this same use of English words in the preface to his *Maighdean an tSoluis* (*MS*), even going so far as to provide Irish substitutes for them in his texts; he lists a number of "Changes made

in the texts" (p. 57) and "Anglicisms" (p. 67). Peadar Ó Ceannabháin in his *Éamon a Búrc: Scéalta* (Baile Átha Cliath 1983) lists (p. 315-6) nearly one hundred borrowings from English in this collection of stories told by this famous Carna (Co. Galway) storyteller.

31. Glenfinn man, Liam Mac Meanman, writes in his Croaghs diary (IFC 295:61) — *"Níor chuala mé duine ar bith de na daoine thart anseo ag caint Béarla go fóill nó níl Béarla fríd an Ghaeilge acu mar atá i mórán áiteacha"* *("I never heard any of the people round here speaking English yet for they do not mix English and Irish as is done in many places.")*.

32. On the disc recordings made in 1948 (cf. Note 15 supra), Anna Nic an Luain *recites* the words of all the songs recorded from her on that occasion. In his diary for 12.6.1947 (IFC 1289: 166-7), Seán Ó hEochaidh writes — *"Giota ar ghiota d'oibir mé liom gur chuir mé Anna i gcionn amhráin . . . Níl siad doiligh a fháil uaithi ach oiread agus nuair a shuífeas sí sa chlúid in aice na tine agus a droim leis an bhalla, ceirtlín an tsnátha ina hucht agus na dealgáin ag ealamairt ar a chéile, is doiligh a sárú a fháil i gcionn scéil nó amhráin siúd is gur i gcionn na n-amhrán is fearr í. Níl an ceol go han-mhaith aici ach is cosúil go raibh sa tseanam nuair atá foinn na n-amhrán ar a fheadalach ag Seán—a fear"* ("Bit by bit, I worked on until I got Anna going at the songs . . . They are not difficult to get from her either and, sitting in the corner by the fire with her back to the wall, a ball of wool in her lap and the needles clicking away, it is hard to find her equal for story and song — though she is best at the songs. She doesn't know the airs very well, but must have done so in the old days, for her husband, Seán, knows them very well indeed."). For an account of Anna Nic an Luain, from whom Seán Ó hEochaidh collected more than two hundred songs, cf. *Béaloideas* 19 (1949), p. 6-7 and 8-28 *passim* for a collection of riddles which he took down from her. *Irland, Heimat der Regenbogen* (Gütersloh 1953), by A. E. Johann, contains a description of the Croaghs and of a visit which the author, accompanied by Seán Ó hEochaidh, paid to Anna Nic an Luain in 1951 (p. 307-20).

The extreme care and attention paid to "wording" songs in this fashion is also emphasized in Pádraig Mac an Ghoill's account of two outstanding informants from Ardara (Co. Donegal) — Róise Nic an Ghoill and Máire Nic Giolla Dé — from whom, in 1935, he took down almost two thousand lines of *"filíocht"* and of whom in *Béaloideas* 8, No. 2 (1938), p. 110, he wrote — *"Níl ceól ag ceachtar aca, agus bhí an bunadh a tháinig rómpa mar a gcéadna. I mbrígh na cainnte agus i gcomhardadh na rann a ba mhó a chuir siad suim, agus de thairbhe sin tá slacht agus cruinneas thar an choitcheanntacht ar a gcuid amhrán agus dán. Sílidh siad gur peacadh marbhthach a bhéadh ann sean-amhrán Gaedhilge a mhilleadh. Nuair a bhíos duine aca ag aithris amhráin ná laoidh' bíonn a' bhean eile, i gclúid duithe féin, á ráidht os íseal le h-eagla go bhfágfaidhe lúb ar bith ar lár."* ("Neither of them has an air nor did their people before them. The meaning of the words and rhyming of the verses is what interested them most and for that reason their songs and poems are unusually exact and polished. They think it a mortal sin to spoil an old Irish song. When one of them is reciting a song or lay, the other is off in another corner wording it quietly for fear something might be left out.").

33. *"Bhí sé ag an fhear a bhí anseo, an t-amhrán sin. Arú, cén t-amhrán nach raibh aige! Bhí deireadh na n-amhrán aige, cinnte, agus bhí an ceol aige, bhí"* (Tape 25/1 SÓC [29.12.1972]).

34. Cf. Note 32, p. xxxiii.

35. For an interesting essay on Seosamh Laoide's career as a collector, written by another collector, cf. C. Bairéad, "Seósamh Laoide", *Béaloideas* 15 (1945), p. 127-40.

36. *"Bhí sé seachtain i nDún na nGall ag fear a bhí ansin a dtugadh siad* Lloyd *air. Agus bhí sé seachtain ansin fá Nollaig bliain amháin ag gabháil cheoil leis go dtí gur thug sé na hamhráin uilig do* Lloyd" (Tape 25/1 SÓC [29.12.1972]).

37. Seosamh Laoide, *Cruach Chonaill* (Dublin 1913), p. 83-4.

38. Cf. IFC Discs M433 (B-C); M434 (A-G); M449 (B-G); M450 (A-B).

39. ". . . *chuaigh mé ar ais chun na gCruach agus chaith mé go meán-oíche ag obair le Seán Mac an Bháird, Micheál Mac an Luain agus Pádraig Mac an Luain"* (IFC 1289:342). I also met Micheál Mac an Luain (Micheál Phádraig) and Seán Mac an Bháird (Johnny John Chiot) during my visits to the Croaghs in the mid-1960s. The former, whom I never heard in story-telling action, had a great reputation locally for *Fiannaíocht.* I heard Seán Mac an Bhaird telling stories in the house of another McLoone family of Crooveenananta (*Bunadh Eoghain Mhícheáil*) with whom he resided at the end of his days and I remember his storytelling style exactly as Seán Ó hEochaidh (IFC 1289:219) and Liam Mac Meanman (IFC 295:66) describe it in their diaries—". . . *baineann sé feidhm as ráite an-ghairid ina chuid scéalta."* (". . . he uses very short phrases in his stories.") and *"Labhrann sé go híseal agus go gasta agus ní thig tabhairt air a ghléas cainte a athrú* ("He talks low and fast and can't be made to alter his way of speaking.").

40. *"Bhí Micheál Mac an Luain ag smaoitiú ar scéal agus bhí Pádraig Mac an Luain ag cuidiú leis agus dúirt Micheál leis stad nó nach raibh sé ach a chur fríd. Ní thiocfadh leis smaoitiú ar scéal nuair a bhíodh daoine eile a bhí istigh ag comhrá agus b'éigean dófa stad ag caint"* (IFC 295:69).

41. *"Bhí fear istigh anocht, Micheál Mac an Luain. Tá scéalta fada Fiannaíochta aige ach ní raibh sé ábalta iad a chur sa mheaisín mar go raibh barraíocht daoine istigh. Tá sé cineál cúthalta ach tá fonn air iad a thabhairt domh. Bhí fear eile ann agus níl uchtach aige a dhul chuig an mheaisín ach oiread. Tá scéalta aige. Bhí a athair, Eoghan Phádraig Mac an Luain, feidhmiúil ag amhráin Ghaeilge"* (IFC 295:73-4). Elsewhere in his diary, Mac Meanman notes (IFC 295: 82)—" *'Seanduine' a bheireadh siad ar an mheaisín"* "('Old man' is what they call the [Ediphone] machine."). Cf. L. Mac Coisdealbha, "Dhá amhrán do'n Edifón", *Béaloideas* 14 (1944),

p. 271-3 where the Ediphone machine is described *inter alia* as a *"gaisgíoch álainn"* ("a lovely hero").

42. *"Béaloideas*—The People's Past" was the name of this 35-minute film, Ireland's entry for the Golden Harp Television Festival in 1977. Máire Pheadair Rua Mhic an Luain, another Croaghs storyteller (cf. *Béaloideas* 31 [1963], p. 152-63), one of Wagner's informants for *LASID* 1 (cf. Note 7, p. xxx), also participated in this programme.

43. The same comment was made to me by another Croaghs storyteller—Micí Mhicheáil Óig Mac an Luain—when I called to see him shortly before he died.

44. *ML 4080, The Seal Woman* formed the centrepiece of his contribution to this programme. The text of that particular telling of the legend was printed (with English and French translations) in the brochure which accompanied the programme for its showing at the Golden Harp Television Festival. Cf. Text 15, p. 28.

45. *"I gceanntar mar na Cruacha, an áit a bhfuil 'ach uile dhuine 'na sheanchaidhe. . ."* (*SCC* 16).

46. Cf. *"scalladóir agus scallaire—Duine beárrtha in theangaidh"*, S. Ó hEochaidh, "Is iomdha duine ag Dia", *Béaloideas* 20 (1950), p. 88.

47. *". . . mar a dúirt mé go minic cheana féin fá Pheadar, níl focal dá dtig amach ar a bhéal nár cheart a scríobh síos. Tá sé ar fhear chomh briathrach agus a casadh riamh domh agus, ar ndóiche, bhí sin sa dúchas aige de réir na gcuntas . . . Rinne mé tamall comhrá agus ba ghoirid uilig gur chuir briathraíocht Pheadair i gcionn pinn mé. Lean mé mar sin ó ghiota go giota agus le scéal fada a dhéanamh goirid, bhí an 11 a chlog ann sular fhág mise Peadar. Bhí lúthgháir mhór orm go dtug mé an chuairt seo air, nó bhí dornán de mhionsheanchas an-suimiúil scríofa agam uaidh. Mar is gnách, níor shíl sé féin go mb'fhiú domh an seanchas seo a scríobh ar chor ar bith, ach in áit mar bhí sin, bhí sé ní ba thábhachtaí ná mórán de na seanscéalta a bhí ag daoine ar fud an bhaile. Bhí cora cainte, seanráite, pisreogaí agus nósaí eile an cheantair uilig ag Peadar agus ba mhór an t-aoibhneas a bheith ag obair leis* (IFC 1289:216-7) . . . *Fear Peadar nach bhfuil scéalta fada ar bith is fiú aige, ach i dtaca le mionseanchas de, ba doiligh a shárú a fháil in áit ar bith. Tá rud eile ann fosta agus is é sin ins an chomhrá choitianta a níos sé nach bhfuil aige ach cora cainte uilig go léir. Ní shílim gur casadh duine ar bith orm in mo shiúlta atá chomh dea-chainteach leis. 'Scalladóir ceart é' mar a deirtear fá dtaobh dó ar na Cruacha. Ar ndóiche, tá sin sa dúchas aige agus tig sé leis mar a thig an snámh leis an lach. Bhí a mhuintir uilig mar sin agus ní hiontas sin, dream a shíolraigh ó na filí. Is goirid amach gaol Pheadair uilig do Thadhg na mBan, an file a bhí sa cheantar fad ó shin"* (IFC 1289:289-90).

For "Tadhg na mBan"—Tadhg Ó Tiománaí—cf. Énrí Ó Muirgheasa, *Dhá Chéad de Cheoltaibh Uladh* (Baile Átha Cliath 1934), p. 324-9.

48. Máire Eoghain Phádraig's comments would seem to indicate that she took the whole business of *"pisreogaí"* quite seriously, whereas Pádraig's cry of *"Sin pisreogaí agat!'* at the end of No. 9 (p. 14) might be taken, perhaps, as an expression of a certain degree of scepticism. Seán Ó hEochaidh in his diary for 9.5.1947 (IFC 1289: 103-4) writes of Pádraig's cousin, Aodh Mac an Luain—*"Tharraing mé orm ceistiúchán Lae Bealtaine le hAodh agus chuaigh mé fríd na ceisteanna uilig leis. Bhí eolas aige ar sheanchas ag baint leis na ceisteanna ach thug mé fá dear air nár mhaith leis a bheith ag rá mórán fá phisreogaí. Tá an creideamh ró-láidir ann agus ní maith leis trácht fá phisreogaí ar chor ar bith."* ("I started on the May Day Questionnaire with Aodh and went through all the questions with him. He knew the lore connected with the questions but I could see that he didn't want to say much about '*pisreogaí*'. His faith is too strong and he doesn't like to talk about them at all.") Similarly, Liam Mac Meanman notes (IFC 295:76)—*"Tá fear sa cheantar seo agus deir sé go gcaithfidh sé nach bhfuil creideamh ar bith agam féin, fear atá i gcónaí ag caint ar dhaoine beaga agus cailleacha pisreogacha."* ("There's a man in this district who maintains I must have no faith, always talking about fairies and superstitious hags.").

49. Cf., for example, other versions of the story *An Crochaire Tarnocht* recorded in the Croaghs (cf. p. 83) or the version published in *MS* by Énrí Ó Muirgheasa, all of which are longer and fuller than the version published here. In reference to Micheál Phádraig Mac an Luain, another Croaghs storyteller (cf. Note 39 *supra*), Liam Mac Meanman notes in his diary for 4.2.1936 (IFC 295:66-7)—*"Thoisigh Micheál Phádraig a chur isteach 'Céadach Mac Rí Tulach' san* Ediphone. *Deir sé go bhfuil sé as cleachtadh. B'éigean dó stad go minic agus hobair nach mbeadh sé ábalta cuimhniú ar an chuid eile de ach fuair sé leis é agus ansin chuir sé isteach 'An Crochaire Tarnocht'. D'éirigh leis níos fearr sa cheann seo. Bhí an fhaitíos ag imeacht de."* ("Micheál Phádraig began recording 'Céadach Mac Rí Tulach' on the Ediphone. He says he's out of practice. He had to make many stops and he was almost unable to remember all of it, but he managed it and then he recorded 'An Crochaire Tarnocht'. He got on better with this one. He was not as timid.").

50. *Béaloideas* 19 (1949), p. 7.

51. Among the latter were the well-known *Lúrpóg larpóg; Aon dó, bligh an bhó* and *Hup, hup a ghearráin doinn.* Cf. also S. Ó Catháin, *Sinsear* (1979), p. 59 for examples of another kind of rhyme taken down from Pádraig—a "*cumhdach*" which lists in amusing fashion alleged courting couples of the district; a number of these were also noted by Seán Ó hEochaidh, cf. "Rannta agus rannscéalta", *Béaloideas* 25 (1957), p. 41-2 and IFC 1032:427, 532 and IFC 1949:66 (= Disc No. M405A).

52. *"Bhal, an cleas a bhí agam ar an urlár, chonaic tú féin é sin. Bhí sé agat chomh luath agus bhí sé déanta. Bhí préata liom sa bhearád i gcónaí agus d'fhágfainn ag an ceann eile é go mbeadh ceathrar cruinn acu i gcuideachta a chéile agam. Chuirfeá síos ceathrar ar an urlár an chéad uair. Agus*

*ansin, bhí na ceithre cinn giota óna chéile. Agus bhí ceann amháin liomsa
sa bhearád i gcónaí. Agus chuirfinn an bearád i gcónaí a raibh an préata
ann agam ar an áit a raibh mé ag cruinniú na bpréataí. Agus chruin-
neochainn na ceithre cinn i gcuideachta a chéile ansin leis an dóigh sin.
Agus bhíodh siad liom sa bhearad i gcónaí nuair a d'fhágfainn iad. 'Siar
chois aibhne, aniar chois aibhne, má tí tú cloch ghlas, nár cheannaí tú
do leas mura ndéanfaidh tú an rud a iarrfaidh mise ort'—déarfá sin achan
uair. Ní raibh ansin ach cineál de phointí, tá fhios agat"* (Tape 85/1 SÓC
[26.12.1973]).

53. I met Micí Simey and his wife Mary Rua there in the mid-1960s and Micí's
brother, John, on and off throughout the 1970s. I recorded some airs and
reels from John while he was staying with *Bunadh Eoghain Mhicheáil*
(McLoones) in Crooveenananta. Liam Mac Meanman, while collecting near
Fintown, noted in his diary for 28.3.1936—(IFC 295:420-1)—"*Tig bean
tincléara isteach agus dhá pháiste léithi agus mála líonta d'araistí stáin—
'pandyannaí cárta' agus 'pandyannaí móra'. Mar is gnách lena leithéid,
labhrann sí go deas séimh le bunadh an toighe. De threibh na nDochartach
í. Sin 'na Simeys' nó tá Simon mar ainm coitianta sa teaghlach i gcónaí.
Bhí siad i gcónaí ag obair ar an stán agus bíonn siad uilig go maith ag
seinm ar an fhideal agus an seancheol ar fad acu. Siúlann siad go státúil
ar an bhóthar agus deirtear go bhfuil siad síolraithe óna ríte.*" ("A tinker
woman with two children and a bag of tin vessels comes in. As she and
her like do, she speaks nicely and gently to the people of the house. She's
a Doherty. That's the 'Simeys'—because of Simon being a common family
name. They always worked tin and they're all good at playing the fiddle
and know all the old music. They walk the road in stately fashion and it
is said they are descended from kings.") A. Feldman and E. O'Doherty,
The Northern Fiddler (Belfast 1979), p. 33-110, contains much material
on this Doherty family, including a musical genealogy, some of their music
and many drawings and pictures of John (Simey) Doherty and his nephew
Simon.

54. There were ten in the family altogether—five brothers (Pádraig, Conall,
Peadar, Eoghan and Micheál) and five sisters (Máire, Maggie, Anna, Kit
and Brigid). Only Maggie and Brigid survive.

55. The local word here and also in neighbouring parts of West Tyrone for
what is elsewhere called an "American Wake" i.e. the night-long party held
for an emigrant about to depart for the New World.

56. Máire died on 20.10.1977, aged 93, and Pádraig, aged 94, passed away
on 8.2.1979. They and their brother, Conall, also aged 94 when he died
on 9.1.1982, lie buried with their people in the graveyard at Edenfinfreagh.

57. *Gramadach na Gaeilge agus Litriú na Gaeilge, An Caighdeán Oifigiúil*
(Baile Átha Cliath 1968).

58. The letters *IFC* and *IFC S* refer respectively to the main manuscript
collection and the Schools' manuscript collection, both of which are in the
Department of Irish Folklore at University College Dublin. The gramophone
disc collection held in the above Department is designated by the prefix
IFC followed by reference to the relevant disc number and track (A,B,C etc).

D'fhág mé i mo dhiaidh ansin ar na Cruacha daoine nár milleadh go dtí seo, daoine múinte macánta, cuid mhór acu nár dhorchaigh teach scoile riamh. Sa cheantar seo, tá saol dá gcuid féin acu, a nósanna féin acu agus an seansaol acu ar fad, an saol atá imithe as cuid mhór d'Éirinn leis na cianta. . . Slán agaibh, a bhunadh na gCruach.*

"I left behind me in the Croaghs a people still unspoiled, gentle and polite, many of whom never darkened a schoolhouse door. In this place, they have a world of their own, their own customs and all the old ways that have long since disappeared from most other parts of Ireland. . . Farewell, people of the Croaghs."

— Liam Mac Meanman, Full-time folklore collector

* IFC 295: 84

1.

"MO DHOIREAGÁN, MO DHOIREAGÁN!"

"Mo Dhoireagán, mo Dhoireagán," ar seisean[1],
"Mo chnó úll agus m'ailleagán;
Agus gur do Ghallaibh atá sé i ndán
A bheith i lár mo Dhoireagáin."

1.

"MY DERRY, MY DERRY!"

"My Derry, my Derry," said he,
"My nutty apple, my trinket;
And that it is foreigners that are destined
To be in the middle of my Derry."

This recording was made on 26.12.1973. Duration 0' 7". Tape 85/1 SÓC (9 cms.p.s.).

1

2.

PÁDRAIG AGUS COLM CILLE

Ach, ar scor ar bith, an t-am a tháinig Naomh Pádraig, an t-am a bhí sé in Éirinn, choisric sé Éirinn thart uilig. Dúirt duine ínteacht leis gur chóir dó a dhul siar go Gleann Cholm Cille. Ní— ní Gleann Cholm Cille a bhí air ins an am sin — níl fhios agamsa c'ainm a bhí air. Ach dúirt sé leis gur chóir dó a dhul siar ar an chontae uilig. Dúirt sé go dtiocfadh fear eile ar an tsaol[1] a rachadh siar ar fad agus ní theachaidh sé ar fad. Agus sin Colm Cille.

2.

PATRICK AND COLM CILLE

So, when St Patrick came, the time he was in Ireland, he blessed all of Ireland. Someone said to him that he should go over to Glencolmcille. It wasn't called Glencolmcille at that time — I don't know what its name was. So, he told him that he should do the whole county. He said that another man would come into the world that would cover the whole county and he didn't do it. And that was Colm Cille.

This recording was made on 29.12.1972. Duration 0' 29". Tape 24/1 SÓC (9 cms.p.s.).

3.

COLM CILLE AGUS "AN BÍOBLA"

Bhí sé i nDoire agus bhí sagart paróiste san áit a raibh sé, i nDoire. Agus bhí bíobla[1] ag an tsagart paróiste agus ba mhaith le Colm Cille an bíobla a bheith *publish*áilte. Agus ní raibh — ní — ní *phublish*áilfeadh sagart na paróiste[2] ar dhóigh ar bith an bíobla a bhí aige.

Agus shuigh Colm Cille go maidin i dteach an phobail, cá bith méid oícheannaí a bhí a dhíth[3] air, leis an bhíobla a *chopy*áil. Agus *chopy*áil sé amach as an leabhar é. Bhí an leabhar i dteach an phobail.

Agus fuair sagart na paróiste amach ansin go raibh an bíobla aige agus thóg sé cogadh air fá dtaobh den bhíobla — go gcaithfeadh sé a thabhairt suas. Agus ní thabharfadh Colm suas an bíobla a bhí aige. Agus d'éirigh eadar an bheirt. Agus d'éirigh an-chogadh eadar an bheirt agus marbhadh[4] mórán daoine ins an rud a bhí ann agus ní thabharfadh Colm suas an bíobla.

Bhal, fágadh ag socrú go deireanach é agus rinne siad amach ag an tsocrú gur leis an chapall[5] a searrach agus gur leis an leabhar[6] a bíobla agus go gcaithfeadh sé an bíobla a thabhairt suas. Agus baineadh an bíobla de.

Agus tugadh *sentence* ansin air, á chur[7] anonn — sílim gur go hIona a cuireadh é. Agus ní raibh cead aige amharc ina dhiaidh nuair a bheadh sé ag imeacht ag Doire ach imeacht leis. Agus chuaigh[8] sé anonn ansin agus chaith sé a shaol ansin ag tiontó ainchríostaíonnaí thall ansin.

3.

COLM CILLE AND "THE BIBLE"

He was in Derry and there was a parish priest there in Derry, where he was. And the parish priest had a bible and Colm Cille wanted the bible to be published. And the parish priest wouldn't publish the bible which he had, on any account.

And Colm Cille sat till morning in the chapel, whatever number of nights was necessary, in order to copy the bible. And he copied it out of the book. The book was in the chapel.

The parish priest found out that he had the bible then and he declared war on him about the bible, to make him give it up. And Colm wouldn't give up the one he had. The two of them went to war about it and a lot of people were killed as a result of it and Colm wouldn't give up the bible.

Well, a settlement was proposed and in the settling of it, it was made out that as the foal belongs to the mare, the bible belongs to its book and that he would have to hand over the bible. So, the bible was taken from him.

And he was sentenced to exile — I think it was to Iona he was sent. And he wasn't allowed to look behind him when he was leaving Derry as he was going away.

And he went over there and he spent his life there converting heathens.

This recording was made on 29.12.1972. Duration 1 ' 42 ". Tape 24/1 SÓC (9 cms. p. s.).

TEACH EOGHAIN PHÁDRAIG IN CROOVEENANANTA

4.

COLM CILLE AGUS ÁR SLÁNAITHEOIR

Bhí cailín aige agus bhí sé amuigh. Ins an tsamhradh, i dtús an tsamhraidh a bhí ann, agus bhí sé amuigh ag cur uisce ar arbhar. Bhí an t-arbhar róthirim ag an aimsir. Agus bhí sé ag cur uisce ar an arbhar.

Agus tháinig duine bocht isteach ionsar an chailín. Agus ní thugadh sé déirce do dhuine ar bith san am sin, Colm Cille. Tháinig duine bocht isteach ionsar an chailín agus — ag iarraidh déirce — agus dúirt sí nach raibh dadaí aicise le tabhairt dó. Dúirt sé go dtiocfadh léithi gráinnín de — bhí sí ag suathadh bonnóg aráin choirce — dúirt sé go dtiocfadh léithi gráinnín den mhin choirce sin a thabhairt dó.

Agus chuir sí a lámh ins an scála agus thug sí slámán den mhin a bhí sí a shuathadh dó. Agus bhuail sé síos i gcroí na tine é. Agus d'fhás tom mór geamhair aníos as an tine, amach as croí na tine.

Tháinig Colm isteach — d'imigh an fear ansin a rinne sin, d'imigh sé — agus tháinig Colm isteach agus d'fhiafraigh sé den chailín caidé an seort an fear a bhí istigh. D'inis an cailín dó agus d'amharc sé ar an rud a bhí sa tine agus chuir sé an-sonrú[1] ann. Agus d'inis sí dó caidé an seort an fear a chuaigh amach agus caidé a rinne sé leis an déirc a thug sise dó.

Agus lean sé an fear a chuaigh amach. Agus chuaigh sé fhad leis. D'aithin sé go maith cé bhí ann, agus chuaigh sé fhad leis agus rinne sé an-ghearán buartha leis ansin agus d'iarr sé maithiúnas. Agus scríob sé an craiceann dá chosa uilig agus chuir sé faoi bhéal pota é, dá loirgneacha, le haithreachas agus le buaireamh fán rud a bhí déanta aige.

Agus tháinig sé chun an tí ansin ar ais agus nuair a thóg sé an pota ansin — níl fhios agamsa cá fhad a d'fhág sé an pota — ach nuair a thóg sé é, luchógaí móra agus luchógaí beaga a tháinig amach as faoin phota. Chuir sé, chuir sé an stuif a bhain sé dá loirgneacha faoin phota.

Agus sin an chéad *start* a rinne Colm Cille le bheith ina naomh.

4.

COLM CILLE AND OUR SAVIOUR

He had a servant girl and he was outside. It was the summer time, early summer and he was out watering corn. The weather had made the corn too dry. And he was watering the corn.

And a poor man came in to the girl. And at that time Colm Cille wouldn't give alms to anybody. The poor man came in to the girl — looking for alms — and she said that she had nothing to give him. She was mixing meal for a scone of oat bread and he said that she could give him some of the meal.

So, she put her hand into the bowl and she gave him a handful of the mixture. And he threw it into the heart of the fire. And a big bunch of oats in the blade grew up out of the heart of the fire.

The man who did that left then and Colm came in and he asked the girl what sort of man had been there. The girl told him and he looked at what was in the fire and he was fascinated by it. And she told him what the man who had just left was like and what he had done with the alms she had given him.

So, he followed after the man who had left. And he caught up with him, recognized him, made his most humble apologies to him and asked for forgiveness. And he scraped the skin from his legs and put it under a pot, he scraped the skin from his shins in regret for what he had done.

I don't know how long he left the pot, but when he came back to the house and lifted the pot, it was mice and rats that came out from underneath it. He put the stuff he scraped from his shins under the pot.

And that's the first start that Colm Cille made at becoming a saint.

This recording was made on 26.12.1973. Duration 2' 20". Tape 85/1 SÓC (9 cms.p.s.).

5.

COLM CILLE AGUS NA BRADÁIN A LEAG É

Tá,[1] bhí sé ag dul trasna[2] ar abhainn amuigh ansin ag ceann Loch Finne. Bhí sé ag dul trasna na habhna ar chlochán ínteacht a bhí ann agus fá Shamhain a bhí ann agus leag na bradáin é ón chlochán.

SÓC Bhíodh na bradáin ann . . .

Bhí na bradáin ag dul siar sa loch, an dtuigeann tú, agus leag siad é. Agus d'iarr sé achaine gan aon bhradán a dhul isteach ins an loch níos mó — níl fhios agamsa ar fhág sé níos mó é, níl fhios agam. Ach ní theachaidh aon bhradán isteach go Loch Finne riamh ó shin.

SÓC Agus níl aon bhradán ann inniu ach oiread?

Tá siad ag dul siar go dtí ceann an locha[3] ach ní théann siad isteach.

5

COLM CILLE AND THE SALMON THAT BOWLED HIM OVER

Well, he was crossing a river out there at the head of Lough Finn. He was crossing over stepping-stones some place there and it was around Hallowe'en and the salmon knocked him off the stepping stones.

SÓC The salmon were . . .

The salmon were going into the lough, you see, and they bowled him over. So, he made the request that no salmon would ever enter the lough again — I don't know whether or not he ordained it should be never again, that I don't know. But no salmon has ever entered Lough Finn since then.

SÓC And there are no salmon in it today either?

They go back to the entrance of the lough, but they don't go into it.

This recording was made on 29.12.1972. Duration 0' 35". Tape 24/1 SÓC (9 cms.p.s.).

6.

TAIRNGREACHT CHOLM CILLE

Bhí an tairngreacht[1] ag Colm Cille atá chóir a bheith[2] istigh.
CEP   Ar mhoithigh tú riamh an tairngreacht—níl fhios agam cé
acu Dónall an Chinn nó Colm Cille a rinne é?
SÓC   Cén ceann, a Chonaill?
CEP   Go mbeadh teach cúirte ar gach cnocán,
Ó, is ea, mhoithigh sé sin!
CEP   Bealach mór i ngach bogach, Buataisí ar gach breallán, Agus
siopa tobac ar mhullach an aird—
Is ea, sin, sin cuid den tairngreacht . . . é sin—
CEP   Agus no cnoic *cover*áilte le crainn nach mbeadh duilliúr ar
bith orthu. Níl duilliúr ar bith ar chrainn an *Forestry*.
Dúirt Colm Cille go dtiocfadh sciúirse roimh an chogadh na
hÉireanna[3] ar na daoine agus gurb é an t-am a thiocfadh sé nuair
a bheadh an drong ar an tsaol a thuillfeadh é. Dúirt sé sin. Bhí sin
ar scor ar bith ins an—ina chuid dá chuid tairngreacht . . . daoine
gan choir gan cháin, go mbeadh na príosúin lán de dhaoine gan choir
gan cháin roimh an chogadh. Dúirt sé sin. Agus tá siad lán anois,
tá, nó chóir a bheith ar scor ar bith, tá.

6.

COLM CILLE'S PROPHECIES

Colm Cille made prophecies which are now almost fulfilled.
CEP   Did you ever hear the prophecies—was it *Dónall an Chinn* or
Colm Cille who made them?
SÓC   Which one Conall?
CEP   That there would be a courthouse on every hillock,
Oh yes, he heard that!
CEP   A road through every bog, Boots on every fool, And a tobacco
shop atop the hill,
Yes, that's part of it.
CEP   And the hills covered with trees with no leaves. There are no
leaves on the Forestry trees.

Colm Cille said that before the Irish war, there would come a scourge and that that scourge would come when the people who deserved it would be on the go. He said that. That was part of his prophecies, anyway . . . innocent and blameless people, that the prisons would be full of innocent, blameless people before the war came. He said that. And they are full now, indeed they are, or, almost full, anyway.

This recording was made on 29.12.1972. Duration 1' 0/". Tape 24/1 SÓC (9 cms.p.s.).

PÁDRAIG EOGHAIN PHÁDRAIG MAC AN LUAIN

7.

BÁS CHOLM CILLE

Agus nuair a tháinig an bás air — bhí seanchapall mór bán aige —
agus bhí an bás ar Cholm agus bhí sé sean, sílim, ins an am. Agus
an lá deireanach a bhí sé go measartha, tháinig an seanchapall isteach
chun an tí agus bhí sí ag cur a cinn anall ina bhrollach agus thart
air uilig go léir. Agus shiúil an seanchapall amach ar ais. Fuair Colm
bás an oíche sin.

D'iarr sé sula[1] bhfuair sé bás a ainm agus a shloinneadh a chur
ar an chomhraidh[2] agus a chaitheamh amach san fharraige. Agus
rinneadh sin. Cuireadh a ainm agus a shloinneadh ar an chomhraidh
agus caitheadh amach san fharraige é.

7.

COLM CILLE'S DEATH

And when he was dying — he had a big old white mare — and Colm
was dying and I think he was old at the time. And on the last day
that he was middling, the old mare came into the house and began
nosing all around his bosom and all about him. And the old mare
walked out again. Colm died that night.

Before he died, he asked for his name and surname to be put
on the coffin and for it to be thrown into the sea. And so it was done.
His name and surname were put on the coffin and it was thrown
into the sea.

This recording was made on 29.12.1972. Duration 0 ' 41". Tape 24/1 SÓC
(9 cms.p.s.).

8.

CÓNAIR CHOLM CILLE

Agus bhí fear thíos fá Inis Eoghain a raibh *lot*[1] mór ba aige. Agus bhí gasúr aige ar fastó[2] a bhí á mbuachailleacht—na mba. Agus chuireadh sé síos fá chladach na farraige iad achan lá.

Agus bhí bó amháin ann agus ní itheadh sí *bit*[3] ar bith féir, bhí sí amuigh ar an ghaineamh[4] ar fad ag lí[5] rud ínteacht. Ní raibh fhios ag an ghasúr agus ní raibh sé ag ligean faic air féin[6] caidé a bhí sí a lí. Agus bhí an bhó ag bisiú ins an bhainne agus ní raibh an méid soitheach a bhí aige ábalta an méid bainne a bhí ag an bhó a choinneáil.[7]

D'fhiafraigh an máistir den ghasúr lá amháin—

"Caidé tá an bhó sin a ithe," a deir sé, "thaire na ba eile achan lá, nó tá an-rud bainne aici? Ní fhaca mé oiread," a deir sé, "ag aon bhó riamh."

"Bhal, níl an bhó sin," a deir an gasúr, a deir sé, "ag ithe *bit* ar bith. Tá[8] sí ag lí rud ínteacht atá amuigh ins an ghaineamh ar fad achan lá, agus ní itheann sí *bit* ar bith."

Chuaigh an fear é féin[9] síos ansin go dtí go bhfeiceadh sé caidé an rud a bhí an bhó a lí. Agus nuair a d'amharc sé thart air agus *strip*áil sé é amach as an ghaineamh, is é comhra Cholm Cille a bhí ansin agus a ainm agus a shloinneadh uirthi agus ordú é a chur in Inis Eoghain.

Agus cuireadh Colm in Inis Eoghain ansin is ní—sin an fad atá agamsa den scéal.

8.

COLM CILLE'S COFFIN

There was a man down in Inishowen who had a lot of cows. And he had a boy hired to herd them. And he used to send them down along the shore every day.

There was one of the cows which wouldn't eat a bit of grass, she was always out on the sand licking at something. The boy didn't know nor did he bother himself about what she might be licking. And the supply of milk from the cow was improving all the time and he hadn't as many vessels as would hold all her milk.

One day, the master asked the boy—

"What's that cow eating every day," says he, "more than the rest of them for she has an awful lot of milk? I never saw," says he, "any cow with as much as her."

"Well, that cow," says the boy, says he, "isn't eating anything. She's forever licking at something out in the sand, but she doesn't eat anything."

The man himself went down then to see what the cow was licking. And when he looked around and when he stripped away the sand, he found Colm Cille's coffin with his name and surname on it with orders for him to be buried in Inishowen.

So, Colm was buried in Inishowen, then and—that's as much as I have of the story.

This recording was made on 29.12.1972. Duration 1' 27". Tape 24/1 SÓC (9 cms.p.s.).

9.

CAILLEACH GHALLDA INA GEARRIA

Bhal, níl fhios agamsa, mná tíre a bhí iontu cosúil leis na mná atá ag dul i gcónaí ach go raibh na, go raibh na geasrógaí seo acu, cá bith cineál dóigh a ndéanfadh siad é.

Bhéaradh siad . . . dá mbeadh ceithre bha[1] agat, nó cá bith méid a bheadh ann, bhéarfadh siad leofa — ní bhe . . . ní raibh aon seort le gnóthú[2] ar bhainne na mba agat ar chor ar bith. Nuair a bhlífeá[3] na ba, ní raibh úsáid ar bith sa bhainne. Ní raibh sé ach searbh agus ní raibh sú nó seamhair ann. Agus bhí an bainne acusan agus an t-im.

Bhí, bhí fear ina chónaí thoir ansin ar an Chlainn Chladhaich ins an áit a raibh, tá fhios agat an áit a raibh Micí s' againne. Ansin a bhí sé ina chónaí agus bhí an baile uilig aige. Agus bhí ocht mba aige. Agus bhí sé ag coimheád achan lá ar ghearria fríd na ba ins an pháirc amuigh. Agus ní raibh fhios aige caidé an t-ábhar a raibh an gearria ann agus ní raibh aon dadaí le gnóthú ar bhainne na mba aige. Ní raibh maith ar bith sa bhainne a bhí acu, ní raibh sé ach mar a bheadh an t-uisce ann.

Bhí cú maith dubh aige agus bhí siad ag ráit[4] go mbéarfadh cú dubh nach mbeadh aon ribe bán inti ar an ghearria. Agus chuaigh sé, chonaic sé an gearria lá amháin fríd na ba agus chuaigh sé amach agus an cú leis agus scaoil sé an cú leis an ghearria.

D'imigh an cú agus an gearria agus chúrsáil sé na páirceannaí uilig i ndiaidh an ghearria. Agus chuaigh sé, chuaigh an gearria de léim isteach ar chlaí[5] a bhí ann, claí mór ard cloch, agus chuaigh an cú de léim isteach ina dhiaidh agus fuair sé greim leise ar an ghearria. Agus, *begorra*, bhris sé leis an ghearria.

Bhí fhios ag an fhear gur, gur rug an cú ar an ghearria agus chuaigh sé fhad leis an áit a bhfaca sé ag dul thar an chlaí é, an gearria — agus bhí an gearria ina — bhí sé — bhí an chailleach ina suí ag bun an chlaí agus an sruth fola léithi, leis an chailligh. Caidé bhí ann ach cailleach ghallda a bhí thíos ins an choill[6] in áit an ghearria a bhí fríd na ba.

Agus tugadh abhaile an chailleach agus fuair an chailleach bás. Agus chuaigh an fear chun na faire.[7] Agus bhí siad ag rann[8] uisce

bheatha[9] ar fhaire na caillí agus tháinig siad fhad leis-sean agus
gloine de leofa. Agus—

"Ól, ól, ól, gloine de bhrat, de bhrat na seanmhná!"

"Ní ólfaidh mise gloine ar bith de bhrat na seanmhná, —mhná,"
ar seisean, "fuair mise mo sháith de bhrat na seanmhná!"

Pisreogaí a bhí ann. Obair an diabhail a bhí ann, obair an
diabhail a bhí ann. Bhí an chailleach ina gearria agus bhí—b'éigean
díthi tiontó ina cailligh agus, *begorra*, hobair go muirbhfeadh an
cú í—mharbh an cú í; fuair sí bás. Agus deir siad gur chóir slat
chaorthainn a bheith ceangailte fána muinéal.[10]

SÓC   Slat chaorthainn?

Is ea. Fáinne caorthainn a bheith ceangailte fá mhuinéal an chú
agus go mbéarfaidh sí níos gaiste ar an—ar an ghearria ansin.

Sin pisreogaí[11] agat!

9.

THE HARE A PROTESTANT HAG!

Well, I don't know, they were just ordinary women like the women
of today except that they knew these spells, whatever way they
worked it.

They used to take . . . if you had four cows or whatever number
you might have, they could take away—you would have no profit
at all off the milk. When you milked the cows, the milk would be
useless. It was just sour and lifeless. And they had the milk and the
butter.

There was a man living out there in Clonclayagh where, you know
where our Mickey used to be. That's where he was living and he owned
the whole townland. And he had eight cows. And every day he could
see a hare in and out among the cows outside in the field. And he
didn't know why the hare was there and he could make no profit
off the cows' milk. The milk they gave was totally useless, it was just
like water.

He had a fine black hound and they used to say that a black hound
without a single white hair would catch the hare. So, one day, he
spotted the hare among the cows and out he went with the hound
and he loosed the hound after the hare.

Off went the hare and the hound and he coursed the fields all around after the hare. The hare gave a leap in over a big high stone wall and the hound leapt after it and he got a hold of the hare by the leg and, begorra, he broke the hare's leg.

The man knew that the hound had caught the hare and he made for the place where he saw the hare jumping over the wall and the hare was—there was the hag sitting by the wall and the blood running out of her. What was it instead of the hare that was among the cows only a Protestant hag that lived down in the wood.

So, the hag was brought home and the hag died. And the man went to the wake. And they were handing out whiskey at the hag's wake and they came up to him with a glass of it.

"Here, drink a glass of the old woman's broth!"

"I'll drink no glass of the old woman's broth," said he, "I got my fill of the old woman's broth!"

It was superstition. It was the devil's work, the devil's work. The hag was a hare and she had to turn back into a hag and, begorra, the hound nearly killed her—the hound did kill her; she died. And they say it should have a rod of rowan-tree round its neck.

SÓC   A rod of rowan-tree?

A rowan-tree collar tied round the hound's neck for it to catch the hare all the faster then.

There's superstition for you!

This recording was made on 19.7.1972. Duration 3' 28". Tape 25/1 SÓC (9 cms.p.s.).

10.

"COME ALL TO ME! COME ALL TO ME!"

Bhí sé — níl fhios agamsa cé acu síos nó aníos a bhí sé ag dul Alt na Péiste ar maidin Lá Bealtaine. Bhíodh siad ag déanamh na bpisreog ar maidin Lá Bealtaine fá choinne tabhairt leofa an bhainne.

Agus bhí cailleach amuigh ins an pháirc agus bhí *chain* iarainn léithi agus bhí sí ag tarraingt an *chain*[1] ina dhiaidh agus —

"Come all to me, come all to me," a deireadh an chailleach.

"The half of it for me," arsa an fear a bhí ag marcaíocht ar an bheathach — bhí sé ag dul an bealach mór.[2]

Agus chuaigh sé — ní raibh de sin ach sin ansin — chuaigh sé abhaile agus, *gorra*, lá arna mhárach, bhí an-*extra* bainne ag na ba. Agus bhí an méid soitheach a bhí aige líonta lán bainne[3] agus bhí sé an-bhuartha.

Agus chuaigh sé fhad leis an tsagart. Agus bhí an-obair aige — bhí an-bhuaireamh air go dtí go bhfaigheadh sé réite den, den rud a bhí déanta aige.

Bhí leath an rud a bhí an chailleach a dh'iarraidh díthi féin, bhí a leath aigesean.

10.

"COME ALL TO ME! COME ALL TO ME!"

Whether he was coming up or going down by Altnapaste on May morn, I don't know. They used to work charms on May morn to steal away the milk.

This hag was out in a field and she had an iron chain with her which she was dragging behind her —

"Come all to me, come all to me," the hag was saying.

"The half of it for me," said the man who was on the road, riding by on horseback.

That was that — he went home and, begorra, next day, the cows gave an enormous amount of extra milk. All the vessels he had were full of milk and he was very worried.

So, he went to the priest. He had a terrible job — he was very worried about getting out of what he had got himself into.

He had got half of what the hag had been asking for herself, that's what he got.

This recording was made on 19.7.1972. Duration 0' 56". Tape 25/1 SÓC (9 cms. p.s.).

SÉAMAS Ó CATHÁIN and PÁDRAIG EOGHAIN PHÁDRAIG MAC AN LUAIN

11.

AN MAISTREADH MÓR

Bhí teach i gCruaich an Airgid agus bhí an bainne ag imeacht as, agus ní raibh — ní — ní thiocfadh im ar bith nó dadaí a dhéanamh den bhainne . . . bhí sé, bhí sé righin agus ní raibh — ní raibh sé mar a bheadh bainne ann ar chor ar bith.

Rinne siad amach go mbuailfeadh siad an maistreadh mór. Agus nuair a bhí an maistreadh cruinn ins an chuinneoig,[1] chaithfí crú asail a dheargadh agus a chur faoin chuinneoig, agus ansin chaithfeadh fear a dhul a choinneáil na cuinneoige agus fear eile a bheadh — ar an bhualadh. Agus fir láidre a chaithfeadh a bheith dá dhéanamh nó thiontóchadh an chuinneog.

Agus chaithfí achan pholl a raibh ar an teach a dhruid, similéir agus deireadh, agus an doras, deireadh a bheith druidte agus ansin fear a dhul a bhualadh agus fear ag coinneáil na cuinneoige agus crú an[2] asail dearg amach as an tine agus é faoin chuinneoig. Agus nuair a thoiseochfaí[3] bualadh an bhainne ansin, ní raibh aon bhuille a rabhthar a bhualadh ar an bhainne nach raibh an crú dearg ag teacht ar an té a bhí ag tabhairt leis an bhainne.

Ach, ní raibh siad tamall[4] ar bith ag bualadh go dtáinig bean chun an dorais agus í ag screadaigh, ag iarraidh an doras a fhoscladh.[5] Agus d'fhoscail siad an doras agus lig siad isteach í. Agus is í bean na comharsana ba deise díofa a bhí ann.

Agus níl sé an t-an-fhad[6] sin den tsaol uilig go léir ó shin é. Bhí aithne mhaith agamsa ar níon díthi, den bhean a bhí ann.

11.

THE BIG CHURNING

There was a house in Silver Hill and the milk was disappearing out of it; it was impossible to make butter or anything out of the milk, it was full of sediment and it wasn't really like milk at all.

They decided to make the big churning. So, when they had gathered the makings of a churning in the churn, a donkey shoe had to be reddened and placed under the churn and, then, one man had to hold the churn and the other do the churning. It took strong men to do it or the churn would fall over.

And every opening of the house had to be closed, chimney and all, and the door — everything had to be closed up and then one man had to start churning and the other to hold the churn with the donkey shoe red hot from the fire underneath it. After that, when the churning commenced, there wasn't a blow that was being struck on the milk that the hot shoe wasn't striking against the person who was stealing the milk.

So, they were only churning a little while when a woman arrived screeching at the door, trying to open the door. So, they opened the door and let her in. And it was the woman of the house next door.

And it's not that long ago either. I knew a daughter of the woman in question well.

This recording was made on 22.4.1973. Duration 1' 19". Tape 24/2 SÓC (9 cms.p.s.).

12.

FIDILÉIR AN AON PHOIRT AMHÁIN AGUS GASÚR DE CHUID NA SÍ

Agus bhí sé ina sheort fidiléara agus ní raibh aige ach aon phort amháin. Ar mhoithigh tú iomrá riamh air?

SÓC Níor mhoithigh.

Ní raibh aige ach port amháin ar scor ar bith agus ní raibh aige ach é féin is a mháthair ins an teach a raibh sé ann. Bhí sé ina chónaí ar an Gharbháin.

Agus bhí—bhí bainis thiar i Leitir Choilleadh agus hiarradh chun na bainse é fá choinne seinm agus ní raibh aige ach port amháin.

SÓC Ní *John Simey* a bhí ann cibé ar bith!

Eh?

SÓC Ní *John Simey* a bhí ann cibé ar bith!

Ó, ní hé ar chor ar bith—ach bhí sé ina fhidiléir ní b'fhearr ná *John Simie* go deireanach. Fan go gcluine tú!

Ach ní raibh dúil aige a dhul agus d'iarr a mháthair air a dhul.

"Bhal, caidé an mhaith domhsa a dhul," a deir sé, "agus gan agam ach port amháin, a sheinm do lucht bainse?"

"Bhal, is cuma," a deir sí, "nuair a hiarradh thú," a deir sí, "gabh."

D'imigh an fear agus an fhideal leis agus nuair a bhí sé ag dul siar in áit ínteacht i Leitir Choilleadh, fá cheann thoir de Leitir Choilleadh, casadh gasúr beag dó. Agus d'fhiafraigh an gasúr dó cá raibh sé ag dul agus d'inis sé dó go raibh sé ag dul chun na bainse agus nach raibh aige ach aon phort amháin agus nach raibh—eagla air nach ndéanfadh sé maith.

"Cá bhfuil an fhideal sin atá agat," a deir sé, "go bhfeice mise í?"

Thug sé an fhideal don ghasúr agus *thune*áil an gasúr suas í agus sheinn sé port agus thug sé dó an fhideal.

"Seinn leat anois," a deir sé, "i Leitir Choilleadh. Níl aon phort a smaointeochaidh tú air," a deir sé, "nach seinnfidh tú anois."

D'imigh an fear agus an fhideal leis. Agus ní raibh aon fhidiléir riamh i Leitir Choilleadh a bhí chomh maith leis an fhear i rith na hoíche ag seinm ar an fhidil. Agus sheinn sé leis agus ní raibh aon phort a gcui. . . smaointeochadh sé air nach gcuirfeadh sé suas chomh maith agus thiocfadh a chur.

Agus chuaigh sé abhaile agus an fhideal leis agus bhí an fh. aige agus bhí an *gift* aige ar fad. Agus bhí sé ábalta seinm 1 gcónaí.

Agus nuair a fuair sé bás—bhí an fhideal crochta ar thaobh an bhalla—bhris an méid cordaí a bhí inti nuair a fuair an fear bás. Agus d'imigh an fhideal ina giotaí fríd an teach. D'imigh. Ar mhoithigh tú sin riamh?

SÓC Níor mhoithigh, níor mhoithigh.

Bhal, bhí sin fíor nó bhí seandaoine i Leitir Choilleadh á inse domhsa, go raibh sé fíor. Fuair sé an *gift*, cinnte.

12

THE FIDDLER WHO KNEW ONLY ONE TUNE AND THE FAIRY BOY

He was a sort of a fiddler and he only knew the one tune. Did you ever hear tell of him?

SÓC No.

Anyway, he only knew the one tune and he and his mother lived alone. He lived in Garvin.

So, there was a wedding over in Letterkillew and he was asked to play at the wedding and he only had the one tune.

SÓC It wasn't John Simey anyway, was it!

Eh?

SÓC It wasn't John Simey anyway, was it?

Oh, indeed, it wasn't, but, in the end, he was a better fiddler even than John Simie. Wait till you hear!

Though his mother begged him, he didn't want to go.

"Well, what good is it for me to go," says he, "to play for the wedding party when I only have the one tune?"

"Well, it doesn't matter," says she, "just go when you were invited."

Off the man went with his fiddle and when he was going along, somewhere back there in Letterkillew, he met a wee boy. And the boy asked him where he was going and he told him he was going to the wedding and that he only knew the one tune and that he was afraid he wouldn't be up to much.

"Where's that fiddle of yours," says he, "till I see it?"

He gave the boy the fiddle and the boy tuned her up and played a tune and he handed the fiddle back to him.

"Play away now," says he, "in Letterkillew. There's not a tune that'll come into your head that you won't be able to play now."

Off the man went with his fiddle. And there was never a fiddler in Letterkillew who was as good as he was on the fiddle, all night long. And he played and played and there wasn't a tune that came into his head that he wasn't able to play as well as it could be played.

So, he went home with his fiddle and he had the fiddle and also the gift of playing. And he could play away all the time.

And when he died — the fiddle was hanging on the wall — all the strings that were in her broke when the man died and the fiddle broke in pieces all over the house, so it did. Did you ever hear that?

SÓC   No, I didn't.

Well, that was true, for the old people in Letterkillew told it to me, that it was true.

This recording was made on 13.4.1972. Duration 2' 16". Tape 66/1 SÓC (9 cms.p.s.).

13

AN SAGART AGUS NA SIÓGAÍ

Dá mbíodh siad in d'éadan, ní bheadh siad intrust. An dtuigeann tú. Ní—ní—ní dhéarfainnse gur daoine maithe iad. Is é an dream a cuirfeadh amach as na Flaithis iad nuair a—nuair a—nuair a bánaíodh é.

SÓC Bhal, cén fáth nár cuireadh go hIfreann iad mar sin?

Bhal, ní raibh siad olc go leor le cur ann.

Chuala mise iomrá ar áit a raibh sagart suas, bhal, suas thiar fá Bhinn Bháin nó amach suas thiar an bealach sin—ó tá sé seal de bhlianta ó shin.

SÓC Cén áit a bhfuil sin, a Phádraig?

Bhal, suas thiar cóngarach ag na Cealla agus bhí sé ag dul ionsar ar dhuine thinn go dtí go ndéanfadh sé *duty* dó ar shiúl oíche agus tháinig beirt acu roimhe[1] agus d'fhiafraigh siad dó an raibh dadaí geallta dófasan. Agus dúirt sé nuair a bheadh sé ag teacht ar ais go n-inseochadh sé dófa agus lig siad ar shiúl ansin é agus d'imigh sé agus rinne sé *duty* don duine thinn.

Agus nuair a bhí sé ag teacht ar ais, bhí siad roimhe ar ais agus tharraing sé amach hancairsean as a phóca agus d'fhiafraigh sé dófa an raibh oiread fola ina nduine[2] ar bith acu agus chuirfeadh deor amháin sa hancairsean. Agus dúirt siad nach raibh. Agus dúirt sé nach raibh dadaí geallta dófa. Agus bhí siad ag ráit gur imigh an bheirt ag caoineadh leofa.

13

THE PRIEST AND THE FAIRIES

You couldn't trust them, if they were against you. Do you see, I wouldn't call them Good People at all. They are really the crowd that was put out of Heaven when it was cleared out.

SÓC Well, why weren't they sent to Hell, then?

Well, they weren't bad enough to be sent there.

I heard of a place where there was a priest—oh, some years ago— somewhere up near Binbane—back up that way.

SÓC Where's that, Pádraig?

Well, up near Killybegs and he was on his way to attend to a sick person by night and two of them appeared in front of him and they asked him if there was anything in store for them. So, he said that he would tell them on his way back and they let him go on his way then and he went on and he attended to the person that was ill.

So, when he was coming back, they were there before him again and he pulled a handkerchief out of his pocket and he enquired if there was as much blood in any one of them as would make a single spot on the handkerchief. So, they said that there wasn't. And he said that there was nothing in store for them. And they say that the two of them made off crying.

This recording was made on 13.4.1972. Duration 1' 24". Tape 66/1 SÓC (9 cms.p.s.).

MAJ UÍ CHATHÁIN, MÁIRE EOGHAIN PHÁDRAIG NIC AN LUAIN and CONALL EOGHAIN PHÁDRAIG MAC AN LUAIN

14

CONALL AGUS NA DAOINE BEAGA

Bhí—bhí an cineál sin ann, na—na—na rudaí sin a dtugann siad na síógaí orthu, bhí siad sin ann cinnte.

SÓC   An raibh áit ar bith thart anseo a mbíodh daoine beaga . . .

Bhal, tá áit a mbíodh siad ann, ach níl thart anseo. Amuigh i Leitir Choilleadh.

SÓC   Cén seort áit a raibh siad ann ansin?

Tá, tá an-rud crann agus tom ann agus rudaí agus bhíodh siad ansin, bhíodh. Agus bhíodh cuid acu ins an áit seo fosta agus níl sé i bhfad ó bhí cuid acu ann.

Bhí Conall an bhliain roimhe lá amháin, chuaigh sé suas—bhí dhá uan a dhíth air—agus chuaigh sé suas chun na—chun na—chun na Leathchruaiche. Sin an baile atá thuas thiar ansin. Bhí sé ag dul a chuartú an dá uan agus chuaigh sé siar—tá seanbhean ina cónaí thuas ansin nach raibh aici ach í féin agus *Joe Burke*. Bhí siad— chuaigh sé isteach chucu agus d'éirigh sé féin agus an tseanbhean amach agus bhí siad amuigh ag an teach.

Agus nuair a bhí sé amuigh ag an teach, chuaigh dhá ghasúr suas ón bhealach mhór, dhá ghasúr agus frocannaí glasa orthu—frocannaí glasa sílim, a dúirt sé a bhí orthu. Chuaigh siad[1] suas ón bhealach mhór, suas bealach mór na Leathchruaiche, agus chuaigh siad suas ansin Baile Thiománaí, agus chuaigh siad suas go raibh siad suas mar a bheadh siad ag dul suas go bun an chnoic.

D'imigh seisean—bhí tráthnóna ceo ann—agus d'imigh sé suas an cnoc a chuartú na n-uan. Agus bhí sé an-mhall, bhí an—bhí solas an lae ag imeacht, bhí sé ag éirí mall nuair a fuair sé an dá uan. Agus thug sé leis iad aniar.

Bhí dúil aige a dhul soir thuas bun an chnoic in aichearra fhad lena chuid talaimh[2] féin agus nuair a bhí sé abhus ag an—tá *wire* thuas ann—nuair a bhí sé abhus ag an *wire*, mhoithigh sé an-scairteach, an-scairteach thuas. Fear thuas ar an chnoc agus fear eile abhus ar a bhun agus an bheirt ag scairtigh le chéile. Ní fhaca sé fear ar bith ar chor ar bith agus bhí sé ag éisteacht leis an scairteach agus shíl sé gur chóir dó a thuigbheáil caidé a bhí siad a rá ach ní thiocfadh leis dadaí a thuigbheáil den rud a bhí siad a ráit ach bhí

siad ag caint leofa. Agus, *begorra, dant*áil[3] sé an dá uan a chur
aniar agus d'fhág sé an dá uan agus tháinig sé anuas abhaile agus
d'fhág sé an — d'fhág sé an *standing* ansin. D'fhág.

Agus bhí siad an an t-am sin — níl sé ach cupla bliain ó shin.
SÓC Cupla bliain ó shin?
Níl sé ach cupla bliain ó shin. Níl.

14

CONALL AND THE LITTLE PEOPLE

That kind, those things they called fairies existed surely.
SÓC Was there any place round here that the little people used
to . . .
Well, there are places where you find them, but not round
here. Out in Letterkillew.
SÓC What sort of place were they in there?
There's a lot of trees and bushes and things and that's where
they were. And there were some of them here in this place too and
not so long ago either.

One day, a year or two ago, Conall went up — he was missing two
lambs — and he went up — up Lacroagh. That townland is back up
there. He was going in search of the two lambs and he went back —
there's an old woman living up there, herself and Joe Burke. They
were — he called in to them and he and the old woman came out of
the house and stood outside.

While they were standing there at the house, two boys came up
from the road, two boys wearing green coats — green coats I think
he said they were wearing. They came up the road, up the road to
Lacroagh and on up the road to *Baile Thiománaí* and on up as if
they were heading up to the foot of the hill.

He carried on — it was a misty evening — he carried on up the hill
searching for the lambs. It was very late, the daylight was fading,
and it was getting late when he found the two lambs. And he took
them back home with him.

He was aiming to go along, back along the hill a short-cut, as
far as his own land and when he was at — there is wire up there —

when he was at the wire, he heard terrible shouting, terrible shouting up above. One fellow up on the hill and another down below and the two of them shouting to each other. He saw no one at all, but he was listening to the shouting which he thought he should be able to understand though he understood nothing of what they were saying as they talked and talked. So, begorra, he was afraid to bring back the two lambs and he left the two lambs there, the both of them and came back home. He just left them.

So, they were there that time — it's only a couple of years ago.

SÓC   A couple of years ago?

It's only a couple of years ago. That's all.

This recording was made on 13.4.1972. Duration 2' 30". Tape 66/1 SÓC (9 cms.p.s.).

CONALL EOGHAIN PHÁDRAIG MAC AN LUAIN, PEADAR Ó DUIBHEANNAIGH, MAJ UÍ CHATHÁIN, MÁIRE EOGHAIN PHÁDRAIG NIC AN LUAIN

E

15

AN FEAR A PHÓS AN MHAIGHDEAN MHARA

Bhal, déarfadh mé giota beag den amhrán duit, ach níl sé agam ar dóigh. Tá—tá an chéad cheathrú agam ar dóigh, agus *trifle* eile de. Agus níl mé ábalta a chur i ndiaidh a chéile ceart. Tá sé an-doiligh, tá sé an-chorrach ar dhóigh ínteacht.

CEP Tá an-Ghaeilge ann.
Tá.

SÓC An raibh mórán ceathrúnacha uilig ann?
Ceithre cinn atá ann agus níl mise ábalta iad a chur le chéile.

SÓC An fear a rinne—an fear a rinne an t-amhrán?
An fear a rinne an t-amhrán.

SÓC Gallchóir é?
Is ea, Gallchóir é, cinnte, is é.

SÓC Agus cé aige ar mhoithigh tusa an rud seo, an scéal sin, a Phádraig?
Ag m'athair a mhoithigh mé é.

SÓC Ag d'athair a bhí sé?
Ó, bhí sé aigesean go maith.

SÓC Bhí an t-amhrán ag d'athair?
Ó, dá *meet*áiltheása eisean, sin an fear a—a bhéarfadh an Ghaeilge duit!

SÓC Is ea, bhí tú ag caint air roimhe.
Bhí seisean ábalta a dhéanamh.

SÓC Cá bhfuair seisean na hamhráin uilig a bhí aige?
Arú, fuair sé ag seandaoine is ag cailleacha a bhí fá na bailte anseo iad, maise. Thart achan áit. Bhí bean ar an Leathchruaich thuas ansin a dtugadh siad Neilí Ní Chormaic uirthi agus fuair sé an-rud acu aici. Agus fuair sé ag achan duine mar sin iad agus bhí— bhí ceol maith aige agus guth maith. Agus d'fheoghlaimneochadh sé rud ar bith de cheol.

Shiúil mé an domhan is ní feas domh go bhfaca mé a leithéid i gcásaibh,
Ach an mhaighdean mhara a bhí ar láimh le Banna agus bhí sí ag síorghealladh grá domh;

A dísbhéal tanaí a chuir smúid ar fhearaibh is ní bréag a bhfuil mise
  a rá libh,
Is gur chúrtha liom a hanál ná na húllaí folláin agus iad a bheith
  i dtaisce le ráithe.

  Sin ceathrú de. Ní thig liom cuimhniú air. Ní thig liom cuimhniú
ar an chuid eile de ar dóigh. Ní thig, ní thig ní thig liom a theacht air.
SÓC Sin an chéad — sin an chéad cheathrú, ab ea?
  Sin an chéad cheathrú de. Fan go bhfeice mé anois. Fan go bhfeice
mé an dtiocfadh liom a theacht ar cheann eile. Níl agam ach beirt
i gcionn — nach bhfuil suaite fríd a chéile.

Nach doiligh domh trácht ar aicíd an ghrá is leannán domh é nach
  scaoiltear,
Is níl duine ins an áit dá bhfeiceadh mo chás nach gcuirfeadh 'gcois
  aird mo chaoineadh;
Is doiligh domh an pháirt a hadhradh go brách le ainnir na séad
  nár síolraíodh,
Is dá dtógthá do lámh is mé a thabhairt ón bhás do gheallúint gan
  spás ní dhéanfainn.

SÓC Maith thú! Bhal, an raibh scéal ar bith ag baint le sin, a
    Phádraig, go raibh fear thart anseo pósta le — le — le bean acu
    sin?
  Bhí sé pósta léithi,[1] ar ndóighe — Gallchóireach thiar i gCaiseal
an Gholláin.
SÓC Cén áit a bhfuil sé sin?
  Caiseal an Gholláin — tá sé thiar ag an Earthainn, an áit a dtugann
siad Caiseal an Gholláin air.
  Agus bhí sé amuigh thíos fán fharraige ar an trá agus chonaic
sé an cailín ina suí ar cloich in imeall an uisce agus í ag cíoradh a
cinn agus bhí an — bhí rud ínteacht leofa a dtugadh siad brat air —
rud ínteacht a bhí acu a raibh siad faoi gheasa aige, an dtuigeann
tú. Agus bhí sin caite fá ghiota díthi — ní raibh sé lena taoibh ar chor
ar bith — agus fuair seisean sin agus thug sé leis é, an rud a dtugadh
siad an brat air.

Fuair sé é agus thug sé leis é agus, *by God,* d'éirigh sise den
charraig agus lean sí é agus chuaigh sé chun comhrá léithi ansin agus
ní thug siad suas an rud a bhí leis ar chor ar bith—bhí sé i bhfolach
aige uirthi—cá bith an rud a bhí ann. Agus chuaigh sé abhaile léithi
agus pósadh é féin agus í féin. Agus bhí sé, an rud seo i bhfolach
i gcónaí aige ar fad, agus bhí cúigear nó sheisear[2] páistí ann—níl
fhios agamsa cá mhéad duine a bhí ann, bhal. Sin rud nach bhfuil
fhios agam.

Agus bhí sé lá amháin ag déanamh cruach arbhair agus thug sé
leis an rud seo agus chuir sé i gcruaich an arbhair é. Agus bhí na
páistí ag coimheád air. Chonaic siad an rud a bhí leis—rud an-deas
ínteacht a bhí ann—chonaic siad an rud a bhí leis á chur i gcruaich
an arbhair. Chuir sé isteach i gcruaich an arbhair é.

Agus lá arna mhárach, d'imigh sé. Chuaigh sé chun an bhaile
mhóir nó áit ínteacht agus ní raibh sé fá bhaile. Agus bhí na páistí
agus ise fá bhaile. Agus dúirt duine acu léithi—

"Bhal, chuir Deá an rud ba deise a chonaic mé riamh," a deir
sé, "i gcruaich an arbhair inné agus tá sé istigh i gcruaich an arbhair
aige," a deir sé, "agus rud an-deas atá ann."

Ní thearn sí faic díreach ach toisiú ar chruach an arbhair agus
leag sí cruach an arbhair agus thug sí léithi an brat ansin agus
d'imigh sí chun na farraige ar ais agus d'fhág sí an Gallchóireach.
Sin an t-am a rinne sé an t-amhrán.

SÓC   Bhal, rinne seisean an t-amhrán, an Gallchóireach?

Rinne seisean an t-amhrán ansin; nuair a tháinig sé abhaile, bhí
sise ar shiúl. Agus leag sí cruach an arbhair agus thug sí léithi an—
cá bith an rud a bhi aici a raibh sí faoi gheasa aige, agus d'imigh
sí ar ais agus—

SÓC   Bhal, ní fhacthas níos mó í?

Ní fhacthas níos mó í, ní fhacthas. Sin é.

SÓC   Bhal, caidé a tharla do na páistí ansin?

Gorra, bhí na páistí aige agus bhí siad aige go raibh siad mór
agus chuala mise an seanduine[3] a bhí anseo ag ráit go raibh aithne
aige ar chuid de na fir.

SÓC   An daoine cearta, mar a déarfá . . .?

Daoine cearta, ní ra . . . daoine *all right,* daoine móra garbha
a bhí iontu, fir mhóra láidre. Daoine cearta cinnte a bhí iontu. Ba
ea.[4]

15

THE MAN WHO MARRIED THE MERMAID

Well, I'll sing a bit of the song for you, but I don't know it all
that well. I know the first verse well enough and another bit of it,
but I'm not able to put it together properly. It's very difficult, it's
very uneven, somehow or other.

SÓC   There's great Irish in it.
       There is.
SÓC   Were there many verses in it altogether?
       There are four in it and I'm not able to put it together.
SÓC   The man, the man made the song didn't he?
       Yes, the man made the song.
SÓC   Who did you hear it from, that story, Pádraig?
       I heard it from my father.
SÓC   Your father had it?
       Oh, he knew it well.
SÓC   Your father had the song?
       Oh, if you had met him, that's the man would have given you
       plenty of Irish!
SÓC   Where did he get all his songs?
       Sure he got them from old men and women around the place
here, all round about. There was a woman up there in Lacroagh
they called *Neilí Ní Chormaic* and he got an awful lot of them from
her. And he got them like that from everyone and he had a great
air and a good voice. And he could learn any kind of singing.

I have travelled the world and never seen anything
Like the mermaid by the Bann who promised me her eternal love;
Her slender lips left men despondent and what I say is no lie,
Her breath I thought sweeter than sound apples stored for a season.

That's a verse of it. I can't remember it. I can't remember the
rest of it properly. I can't, I can't quite get it.
SÓC   That was the first verse, was it?
       That's the first verse. Wait till I see now. Wait till I see can I
remember the other one. There are only two of them that I know,
that I haven't got mixed up.

Is it not hard for me to speak of love, an affliction from which I
   cannot be relieved?
There's not one in the place who knew my situation but would
   loudly lament for me;
It is hard for me to maintain my love for the maiden of the treasures
   who was not of human descent,
And were you to raise your hand and save me from death I would
   never take anyone but you.

SÓC   Good man! Well, was there a story associated with that,
      Pádraig, about a man from round here who was married to
      one of those women?

   He was married to her, surely — a man called Gallagher back in
Cashelgoland.

SÓC   Where's that?

   Cashelgoland — it's back at Narin — a place called Cashelgoland.

   He was down by the sea, on the beach and he saw this girl sitting
on a rock at the water's edge combing her hair and the — there was
something they call the cloak, something that held them under a spell,
do you see. And that was lying nearby — it wasn't beside her at all —
and he got that and he took it with him, this thing they call the cloak.

   He got it and he took it with him and, by God, she got down
off the rock and she followed him and then he fell to talking with
her and he didn't hand over the thing at all — he had it hidden from
her — whatever it was. And he went on home with her and they got
married, the pair of them. And all the time, he kept this thing
hidden and they had five or six children — to tell the truth, I don't
know how many they had. That's something I don't know.

   So, one day he was making a corn stack and he took this thing
and he hid it in the corn stack. And the children were watching him.
They saw what he had — it was something very nice — they saw him
putting this thing he had into the corn stack — he put it in the stack
of corn.

   So, next day he went off somewhere. He went to town or some
place and was away from home. And she and the children were at
home. And one of them said to her —

   "Well, Daddy put the nicest thing I ever saw," says he, "into the
stack of corn yesterday and he has left it in the stack of corn," says
he, "and it's very nice."

Right away, she just started on the corn stack and tumbled it and she got the cloak and then she went back to the sea and she left Gallagher. That's when he made the song.

SÓC Well, Gallagher made the song, did he?

He made the song then; when he came home, she was gone. She tumbled the corn stack and she took whatever it was that was holding her under the spell with her and away she went.

SÓC Well, she was never seen again?

She was never seen again, never. That's it.

SÓC Well, what happened to the children then?

Goodness, he had the children and he had them till they grew big and I heard my old father say that he knew some of the men.

SÓC Well, were they, as you might say, proper people?

Proper people, indeed, not a—perfectly all right, big rough people they were, big strong men. Yes, proper people, surely. Yes, indeed.

This recording was made on 13.4.1972. Duration 5' 51". Tape 66/1 SÓC (9 cms.p.s.).

16

AN SIOSÁNACH

Bhí sé stoptha i dTaobh an Locha amuigh ansin ag duine ínteacht a bhí ann—An Siosánach.

SÓC An Siosánach?

An Siosánach. Agus bhí sé stoptha i dTaobh an Locha agus bhí sé i gcónaí ag déanamh *bow and arrows,* ag déanamh cipín agus ag cur barr orthu. Agus bhí sé ina shuí fán tine agus é ag déanamh na rudaí sin leis ar feadh¹ blianta.

Agus lá, lá amháin go deireanach, bhí rud—bhíodh—thigeadh na Connachtaigh anuas agus thógadh siad an rud a dtugadh siad Creacha Baiollach air; Creacha Baiollach. Sin—thógadh siad— scaoileadh siad amach na ba agus thiomáineadh siad leofa iad, *lot* eallaigh. Scaoileadh siad cupla ceann amach as achan teach agus thiomáineadh siad leofa iad. Bheireadh siad leofa iad.

Ach, *begorra,* tháinig siad aniar Taobh an Locha agus bhí an Siosánach ann i gcónaí. Agus chuaigh siad chun an bhóithigh agus scaoil siad amach cupla bó agus thiomáin siad leofa iad.

Bhí bean an tí, bhí sí fríd an teach agus bhí an Siosánach ag an tine agus—

"Imigh leat," a deir sí, "amach as mo chasán," a deir sí. "Is beag— tá tú ag déanamh cipín ansin," a deir sí, "le seacht mbliana agus is beag an éadáil inniu thú."

Ó, a bhean mhallaithe," a deir sé, "dá mbítheá² i do thost," a deir sé, "bhí na geasa díom," arsa an fear, arsa an Siosánach. "A bhean mhallaithe," a deir sé, "dá mbítheá i do thost, bhí na—bhí na geasa díom."

D'éirigh sé ina sheasamh agus chruinnigh sé suas a chuid cipín agus bhí na—bhí na Creacha Baiollach ar shiúl soir.³ Bhí an—bhí an t-eallach tógtha agus iad ar shiúl agus iad leofa. Agus d'iarr sé ar fhear an tí a bheith leis agus lean sé iad soir.

Agus nuair a tháinig siad fhad le Bealach na gCreach—sin an t-ábhar a bhfuil Bealach na gCreach air ó shin—nuair a tháinig siad fhad le Bealach na gCreach, fuair siad fhad leofa.

"Cé acu a choiscfeas tú an namhaid," ar seisean, "nó a cheapfas tú an chreach?"

"Ceapfaidh mé an chreach," arsa an fear.

Thúsaigh an Siosánach a scaoileadh na gcipín, cá bith an cineál cipín a bhí déanta aige, thúsaigh sé á scaoileadh — na gcipín agus choisc sé an namhaid. Agus chuaigh an fear roimh an eallach agus thiontóigh sé an chreach. Agus chuaigh siad siar agus an t-eallach leofa ar ais agus nuair a bhí siad chóir a bheith thiar, dúirt an Siosánach —

"Bhal, tá mise réidh[4] leat anois," a deir sé. "Tá mé ag dul do d'fhágáil."

"Siúil leat liomsa," a deir sé, "agus bhéarfaidh mé an chéad chuid d'achan seort deoch agus greim a mbeidh agam duit fad agus mhairfeas tú," arsa seisean leis an tSiosánach.

Chuaigh an Siosánach leis ansin agus chuaigh sé chun an tí agus chuaigh an fear chun an tí. Bhí tart ar an fhear agus d'iarr sé deoch bhainne. Thug a bhean deoch dó agus d'ól sé é agus ní thug sé dadaí don tSiosánach.

"Tím," arsa an Siosánach, ar seisean, "tá mise fada go leor anseo. Ní bheidh mise níos faide ann. Sin an chéad deoch," a deir sé, "agus ní thug tú dadaí domhsa."

Agus chruinnigh an Siosánach suas a chuid cipín agus d'imigh sé agus d'fhág sé ar fad é.

"Tá mise réidh leat anois," a deir sé, "go Lá Thadhg na dTadhgann" — cá bith fad é go dtige an lá sin.

16

THE HISSER

He was staying with someone out there in Tievelough — "The Hisser".

SÓC The Hisser?

The Hisser. He was living out in Tievelough and he was always making "bows and arrows", making little sticks and putting a point on them. And for years on end, he sat by the fireside making those things all the time.

One day, there was — the men of Connacht used to come down to Donegal and they used to make something they called The Boylagh

Seizure; the Boylagh Seizure. That is to say, they used to take—they'd let out the cows and drive them off, a whole lot of cows. They'd let out a couple from every house and drive them away. They'd take them away with them.

So, begorra, they came along by Tievelough and the Hisser was there as always. And they went into the byre and loosed a couple of cows and drove them away.

The woman of the house was running up and down the house and the Hisser was at the fire and—

"Away with you," says she, "out of my way," says she. "You are little—you're making arrows," says she, "these seven years—and you are of little use today."

"Oh, accursed woman," says he, "if you had only held your tongue," says he, "I would have been released from enchantment," says the man, says the Hisser. "Accursed woman," says he, "if you had only held your tongue, I would have been released from enchantment."

He stood up and gathered up his arrows and the Boylagh Seizure had passed by. They had seized the cattle and gone their way. So, he asked the man of the house to come with him and he followed after them.

When they got as far as *Bealach na gCreach* ("The Route of the Seizures")—that's why it has ever and always been called *Bealach na gCreach*—they caught up with them when they got to *Bealach na gCreach*.

"What do you want to do," says he, "halt the enemy or capture the seizure?"

"I'll capture the seizure," says the man.

The Hisser began shooting the arrows, whatever kind of arrows he had made, he began shooting them and he halted the enemy. And the man got in front of the cattle and turned them about. Back they went with the cattle and when they were nearly there, the Hisser said—

"Well, I'm finished with you now," says he. "I'm going to leave you."

"Come along with me," says he, "and I'll give you the first of every kind of food and drink I get, as long as I live," says he to the Hisser.

The Hisser went with him then and he went into the house and so did the man. The man was thirsty and he called for a drink of milk. The wife gave him a drink and he drank it up and offered none to the Hisser.

"I see," says the Hisser, says he, "I'm long enough here. I'll stay no longer. That's the first drink," says he, "and you gave me none of it."

So, the Hisser gathered up his arrows and off he went and left them altogether.

"I'm finished with you now," says he, "till Tibb's Eve" — however long it may be till that day comes.

This recording was made on 13.4.1972. Duration 3' 24". Tape 66/1 SÓC (9 cms.p.s.).

MÁIRE EOGHAIN PHÁDRAIG NIC AN LUAIN

17

CLAINN tSUIBHNE NA MIODÓG

Bhal, an t-am a bhí na — na — na *Danes* in Éirinn, ar mhoithigh tú iomrá air?
SÓC Mhoithigh.

An t-am a bhí siad in Éirinn i bhfad ó shin, ní raibh aon lánúin dá bpósthaí nach gcaithfeadh fear acu a bheith ina luí ag an *bhride* an chéad oíche. Ar mhoithigh tú iomrá air sin riamh?
SÓC Níor mhoithigh, níor mhoithigh, níor mhoithigh.

Níor mhoithigh tú sin riamh? Níor mhoithigh! Chaithfeadh siad a bheith ina luí ag an *bhride* an chéad oíche.

Agus rinne siad suas am amháin — chuir siad dlí leis an rud fosta ins an am sin — rinne siad suas, pósadh *lot* lánúineach — naoi gclaigne, sílim, a pósadh acu — de Chlainn tSuibhne. Clainn tSuibhne a — a bhí — bhí ar — sa dream a pósadh.

Agus fuair siad gasúr beag a raibh gruag[1] mhaith fhada air agus cíoradh síos é agus *fit*áileadh suas é. Agus bhí fear acu fá choinne a dhul a luí ag achan *bhride* ins an oíche, in áit na — in áit na m*bride*annaí, an dtuigeann tú, a dhul a luí ag achan — ag achan *Dane*. Bhí na *Danes* fá choinne fear a bheith ag achan *bhride* ins an oíche agus bhí na — bhí na bhí na diúlaigh seo *fit*áilte fá choinne — in áit an *bhride*.

Agus bhí scian[2] le achan duine. Agus nuair a chuaigh siad a luí san oíche, chuir achan fhear a scian ins an bholg ag an — ag an *Dane* agus mharbh siad na — na — na naoi gclaigne *Danes* in oíche amháin.

Agus is é an t-ainm a — an t-ainm a bheireadh siad orthu ina dhiaidh sin ó shin — Clainn tSuibhne na Miodóg.

17

CLAN SWEENEY OF THE DAGGERS

Well, did you ever hear tell of the time the Danes were in Ireland?
SÓC I did.

Long ago when they were in Ireland, there wasn't a couple that got married but one of them had the right to spend the first night with the bride. Did you ever hear tell of that?
SÓC No, I didn't, I didn't.

You never heard of that? You didn't! They had to get spending the first night with the bride.

They made up once—they made it the law too at that time—they made up—a whole lot of couples of the Sweeney Clan got married, nine of them, I think. The ones that got married were called Sweeney.

So, they got a wee boy with nice long hair and they combed him and dressed him and they had one of these for going to bed that night with the brides, instead of the brides, do you see, for going to bed with each Dane. The Danes were to have one of their men with each of the brides that night and these lads were fitted out to take the place of the brides.

So, each of them had a knife. And when they went to bed that night every one of them stabbed a Dane in the belly and they killed the nine Danes in one night.

And the name, the name they were called ever after was Clan Sweeney of the Daggers!

This recording was made on 13.4.1972. Duration 1' 47". Tape 66/1 SÓC (9 cms.p.s.).

18

AN FEAR MÓR

Bhal, bhí fear ag dul thart anseo fad ó shin a dtugadh siad an Fear Mór air. Agus bhíodh sé ag aíochtaigh ó theach go teach, eadar na tithe. Agus bhí buachaill óg ina chónaí ann, mar a bheadh sé sa teach seo, agus bhí cailín ins an teach sin thall agus bhuail sé i ngrá léithi agus pósadh an bheirt.

Agus bhíodh sé anonn is anall — agus bhí seanduine thall agus ní itheadh sé mórán uilig nuair a bhíodh an bia réidh. Ní bhíodh ann ach go mbeadh siad ina suí ag na, ag na pré́ataí[1] — bascóid a bhí acu agus í ar bhéal an phota i lár an tí, agus sin an cineál dóigh a raibh na dinnéir á dhéanamh[2] — d'éiríodh an seanduine sula mbeadh dhá phréata ite ag an fhear óg agus thógadh sé an bhascóid agus chuireadh sé i dtaisce í. Agus ní bheadh dadaí ite ag an fhear óg ar chor ar bith a raibh maith ar bith ann. Agus bhí sé lag leis an ocras nuair a bhíodh sé ag teacht anall. Agus i gcónaí ag dul anonn dó, léimeadh sé an abhainn agus ag teacht anall dó i gcónaí, shiúladh sé í.

D'fhiafraigh duine ínteacht dó caidé an t-ábhar, d'fhiafraigh an *Big Man* dó caidé an t-ábhar a shiúladh sé an abhainn ag teacht anall dó agus a léimeadh sé í ag dul anonn dó. Dúirt sé leis go mbíodh sé chomh lag leis an ocras ag teacht anall dó agus nach dtiocfadh leis an abhainn a léimeadh[3] agus go gcaithfeadh sé í a shiúl — go raibh seanduine thall ansin agus nach mbeadh dhá phréata ite aigesean nó go dtí go dtógadh sé an bhascóid agus go stadadh sé a dh'ithe agus nach mbeadh leath a sháith ite aigesean, agus go mbíodh sé lag leis an ocras ag teacht anall dó.

"Leigheasfaidh mise sin," arsa an Fear Mór, "ins an oíche amárach."

Chuaigh an Fear Mór anonn agus d'iarr sé lóistín agus fuair sé é. Agus nuair a bhí an suipéar réidh — suipéar préataí, is cosúil, a bhí acu, bhí an bhascóid i lár an tí agus an pota fúithi — chaith an *Big Man* amach an méid préataí a bhí ar an bhascóid ionsar na madaidh agus níor fhág sé aon cheann istigh ann nár chaith sé amach ionsar na madaidh fríd an teach. Agus d'ith siad iad agus ní raibh dadaí ag an tseanduine ansin le fáil go maidin.

Rinne an Fear Mór, rinne sé a leaba bheag suas i dtaobh an tí agus luigh sé ann. Agus chuaigh an seanduine a luí i leaba na clúdach mar sin, mar tá an leaba sin — agus — é féin agus an chailleach. Agus siar deireadh na hoíche, bhuail an seanduine uille ar an chailligh —

"Éirigh, a bhean údaí," a deir sé, "agus déan braon, déan réidh rud ínteacht domhsa a íosfas mé; tá mé chóir a bheith *done* leis an ocras," arsa an seanduine.

D'éirigh an chailleach agus rinne sí pota beag bracháin — pota beag a bhí aici — rinne sí brachán ann agus d'fhág sí thíos ag an doras é go dtí go bhfuaraíodh sé. D'éirigh an Fear Mór agus chuaigh sé síos chun an dorais agus rinne sé a mhún sa phota. Ní thiocfadh leis an tseanduine an brachán a ól ansin — bhí a mhún déanta ag an tseanduine[4] sa phota.

Agus chuaigh an chailleach a luí ar ais agus fá chionn tamaill eile ina dhiaidh sin, bhuail an seanduine uille ar an chailligh —

"Éirigh, a bhean údaí," a deir sé, "agus déan réidh rud ínteacht domhsa. Ní bheidh mé beo ar maidin leis an ocras."

D'éirigh an chailleach agus rinne sí toirtín agus tharraing sí aniar an ghríosach agus chuir sí an toirtín faoin ghríosaigh go dtí go mbruithfeadh sí é. D'éirigh an Fear Mór agus shuigh sé ag an tine.

"Fan thusa i do luí," ar sise, "is é mo bhuaireamh féin a bheir i mo shuí mise."

"Ó, is é ár mbuaireamh féin," a deir sé, "a bheir inár suí uilig sinn. Bhí triúr mac agamsa," a deir sé, "agus bhí *farm*[5] maith talaimh agam. Agus rann mé eadar an triúr é. Rinne mé claí mar sin," a deir sé, "agus claí mar sin, agus claí mar sin, agus ní ghlacfadh aon duine acu aon *bhit* de na trí *chut*" — agus an maide briste[6] aige — "rinne mé, rinne mé smic smaic, smic smaic," a deir sé, "de dheireadh" — é istigh fríd an toirtín ins an tine. Agus stróc sé an toirtín uilig fríd an luaith agus ní thiocfadh aon *bhit* a ithe ansin de.

Chuaigh an chailleach a luí ar ais agus chuaigh an seanduine a luí. Nuair a bhí siad gearrthamall[7] ina luí is bhí an lá chóir a bheith ann, bhuail an seanduine uille ar an chailligh —

"Éirigh, a bhean údaí," a deir sé, "agus gabh suas, gabh chun an bhóithigh," a deir sé, "agus bligh an bhó, nó ní bheidh mise beo ar maidin leis an ocras."

D'éirigh an chailleach agus chuaigh sí amach chun an bhóithigh a bhleaghan[8] na bó. Agus níor fhan an Fear Mór i bhfad uilig ina

luí nuair a mhoithigh sé ag dul amach í go dtí gur éirigh sé agus
chuaigh sé amach.

"Ó, a bhean údaí," a deir sé, "ná nach bhfuil an bainne blite
go fóill agat—tabhair domh braon den bhainne," a deir sé, "nó ní
sheasóchaidh mise seo."

Thug sí dó an méid bainne a bhí blite aici agus d'ól sé é agus
tháinig sé chun an tí. Agus ní raibh an chailleach ag teacht isteach.
Rinne sí amach go mblífeadh sí an bhó amach. Agus d'éirigh an seanduine agus chuaigh sé féin amach. Agus chuaigh sé chun an bhóithigh
agus—

"Nach bhfuil an bhó blite go fóill agat?" a deir sé.

"Arú," a deir sí, "imigh leat," a deir sí, "a ghlugaí shalaigh," a
deir sí, "ar ndóighe, thug mé braon den bhainne duit cheana féin,[9]
nach gcaithfidh sé go mbeadh do sháith ann!"

"Ó, ní mé a bhí ann ar chor ar bith," a deir sé, "is é an boc atá
istigh a bhí ann. Cuirfidh mise *finish* anocht air!"

Nuair a fuair an Fear Mór amuigh é—bhí gamhain óg istigh
ann—thug sé leis an gamhain agus chuir sé ins an tsráideoig é ins
an áit a raibh sé ina luí agus chuaigh sé féin in áit an ghamhna i
gcúl an dorais.

Agus tháinig an seanduine isteach agus *weapon* leis agus thoisigh
sé ag bualadh an ghamhna, agus bhuail sé leis é go dtí gur mharbh
sé an gamhain. Agus—

"Is tú an fear amaideach," ar siesean, "ag marbhadh do ghamhna
ar mhaithe liomsa."

Agus léim sé amach ar an doras agus d'imigh sé leis.

D'fhág sé an seanduine agus an chailleach ansin agus am ar bith
a dteachaidh an fear óg anonn chun an tí thall ina dhiaidh sin, bhí
a sháith le hithe le fáil aige agus ní raibh an seanduine ag tógáil na
bascóide ar chor ar bith. Bhí deireadh thart agus bhí dóigh mhaith
air ó sin amach.

18

THE BIG MAN

Well, there was a man going round here, long ago, they called
The Big Man. And he used to be lodging in different houses, from
one house to the next. And there was a lad living there, say, in this

house here and there was a girl living in that house over there and he fell in love with her and they got married.

And they used to be back and forward — and the old fellow in the far house used to eat very little food at mealtime. They would just have sat down to the potatoes — it was a basket they had laid on top of the pot in the middle of the kitchen and that's the way they took their dinner — when the old man would get up before the young man had eaten more than a couple of potatoes and he'd lift the basket and put it away. And the young man would hardly have eaten anything worth talking about. And he was weak with hunger coming back. And when he was going over, he'd jump the river, but coming back he waded it, always.

Someone — the Big Man asked him why he waded the river on his way home and jumped it on his way over. He said he was weak with hunger on his way back and that he wasn't able to jump the river but had to wade it — telling him about the old man who would remove the basket and stop eating when he had only managed to eat a couple of potatoes, not nearly his fill, and that he was weak with hunger coming back.

"I'll fix all that," said the Big Man, "tomorrow night."

The Big Man went across and asked for lodgings and got them. And when supper was ready — it seems it was potatoes for supper — the basket was in the centre of the floor, with the pot underneath it. And the Big Man threw all the potatoes that were in the basket to the dogs not leaving a single one that he didn't scatter to the dogs here and there in the house. And they ate them and there was nothing left for the old man till morning.

The Big Man then made his bed up by the wall and stretched out there. And the old man went to bed in the outshot, just like that one over there, he and his old wife. And well on in the night the old man gave the old woman a dig with his elbow —

"Rise up, woman," says he, "and make a drop, prepare something for me to eat; I'm nearly dead with hunger," says the old man.

The old woman got up and made a little pot of porridge — it was a small pot she had — she made the porridge and left it down by the door to cool. The Big Man got up and went down to the door and pissed in the pot. The old man couldn't sup the porridge then for the old fellow (*recte* "The Big Man") had pissed in it.

F

The old woman went back to bed and after a little while the old man hit her a dig with his elbow.

"Rise up, woman," says he, "and prepare something for me to eat, I'm so hungry I won't survive till morning."

The old woman got up and she made a scone of bread and she pulled out the coals and placed the scone under them to bake. The Big Man got up and sat by the fire.

"You go back to bed," says she, "It's my own bother that has me up."

"Oh," says he, "It's all our bother that has us all up."

"I had three sons," says he, "and I had a good farm of land. And I divided it between the three of them. I made a fence like that," says he, "and one like that and another like that and none of them would agree to any of the three divisions;" — and he had the tongs — "I made mish mash, mish mash of the whole lot," says he — back and forward through the scone in the fire. And he made bits of the scone in the ashes and you couldn't eat any of it.

The old woman went back to bed and the old man too. When they had been a good while in bed, it was getting near day and the old man hit the old woman a dig with his elbow.

"Rise up, woman," says he, "and go up to the byre and milk the cow for I'm so hungry I won't survive till morning."

The old woman got up and she went out to the byre to milk the cow. And the Big Man didn't stay long in bed when he heard her going out, but got up and followed her out.

"Oh, woman," says he, "have you not finished milking yet? Give me a drop of it," says he, "for I can't stand this."

She gave him whatever she had milked and he drank it and went back to the house. The old woman was still outside. She decided she would finish milking the cow. So the old man got up and *he* went out. He went to the byre and —

"Haven't you milked the cow yet?" says he.

"Away out of that with you," says she, "you dirty glutton, didn't I give you milk already! Surely, that's enough for you."

"Oh, that wasn't me at all," says he, "it was the boyo inside. I'll do for him this night!"

When the Big Man had him outside — there was a young calf within — he took the calf and put it in the shakedown where he had been lying and he stationed himself where the calf had been behind the door.

The old man came in with his weapon and began beating the calf and he hammered the calf till he killed it.

"You're the foolish man," says he, "to have killed your calf because of me."

And he jumped out the door and away he went. He left the old man and woman there and any time the young man went over to the house after that, he got plenty to eat and the old man never removed the basket. That was that and all was well with him ever after.

This recording was made on 2.12.1973. Duration 6' 00". Tape 85/1 SÓC (9 cms.p.s.).

19

AN CROCHAIRE TARNOCHT

[Bhí] rí ann fad ó shin agus bhí níon aige agus bhí sí le fáil ag fear ar bith a mhuirbhfeadh trí fathaigh a bhí sa Domhan Thoir agus a bhéarfadh na cinn anoir[1] agus a d'fhágfadh síos ag an teach aige iad go socair suaimhneach.

Agus bhí fear ann arbh ainm dó Cormac Mhic Rí an Ealla. D'éirigh Cormac maidin amháin agus chuir sé air a chulaith chatha agus a chrua chomhraic. Bhí a scian ina láimh chlí agus a chlaíomh síos siar leis agus ní thearn sé stad mara nó cónaí go raibh sé ag an Chrochaire Tharnocht.

"Buail buille sa tsealán," arsa an Crochaire, "agus lig anuas mé," a deir an—

"Bóthaistear briathar,"[2] a deir sé, "ní mé a chuir suas thú agus ní mé a ligfeas anuas thú."

D'imigh Cormac leis agus níor stad sé go raibh sé ins an Domhan Thoir. Agus níorbh fhada a bhí sé ansin gur mhoithigh sé an— búirtheach an fhathaigh ag teacht. Tháinig an fathach agus tífeá an domhan brách eadar a dhá chois agus ní fheicfeá dadaí os cionn mhullach a chinn, bhí sé chomh hard sin. Bhuail sé féin agus Cormac le chéile agus nuair a bhí siad tamall ag troid—

"A ghaiscígh óig amaidigh," ar seisean, "ná marbh amach mé agus bhéarfaidh mé an tseantua bhriste bhearnach atá faoi cholbha mo leapa duit."

"Is liom féin é sin," arsa Cormac, "ó do lá-sa amach."

Bhuail Cormac buille i gcomhrac a chinn agus a mhuinéil air agus bhain sé an ceann de. Agus thug sé leis an ceann agus tháinig sé anoir agus an ceann leis go dtí go raibh sé ag an Chrochaire Tharnocht. Bhí an Crochaire thuas ins an tor agus ní raibh bealach anuas aige.

"Bhuail buille sa tsealán nuair a d'éirigh leat chomh maith agus d'éirigh," ar seisean, "agus lig anuas mé."

"Ní mé a chuir suas thú agus ní mé a ligfeas anuas thú," arsa Cormac.

Chuaigh Cormac go cúl teach an rí agus d'fhág sé síos ceann an fhathaigh go socair suaimhneach ag cúl an tí agus chuaigh sé isteach go dtí an doras.

"Tá an—trian do níne bainte agam," ar seisean leis an rí.

"Maith go leor," arsa an rí.

Chuaigh Cormac abhaile agus luigh sé an oíche sin. Agus nuair ba luath a d'éirigh an lá, ní luaithe ná d'éirigh Cormac. Nigh sé a aghaidh agus a lámha, chuir sé air a chulaith chatha agus a chrua chomhraic agus bhí a scian ina láimh chlí agus a chlaíomh síos siar leis. Agus ní thearn sé stad mara nó cónaí go raibh sé ag an Chrochaire Tharnocht.

"Buail buille sa tsealán," arsa an Crochaire, "agus lig anuas mé."

"Ní mé a chuir suas thú agus ní mé a ligfeas anuas thú."

Ní thearn sé stad mara nó cónaí go raibh sé ins an Domhan Thoir ag na fathaigh. Níorbh fhada a bhí sé ann gur mhoithigh sé an fathach ag teacht. Agus nuair a tháinig an fathach chomh fada leis—

"Mharbh tú mo dheartháirse inné," ar seisean, "ach ní rachaidh leat inniu," a deir sé. "Cuirfidh mise deireadh[3] leat inniu. Cé acu is fearr leat greimeannaí caola cruaidhe coraíocht nó *snap*annaí chlaíomh in easnacha a chéile?"

"Is fearr liom greimeannaí caola cruaidhe coraíocht," arsa Cormac. "Is é a chleacht mé i mbaile bheag, i mbaile mhór, i ngleann m'athara agus mo mháthara féin riamh."

Bhuail an bheirt lena chéile agus nuair a bhí neoin beag[4] agus deireadh an lae ann, chuir Cormac ar a ghlúin é. Tharraing sé air a chlaíomh agus bhuail sé i gcomhrac a chinn agus a mhuinéil é agus bhain sé an ceann de.

Thug sé leis an ceann agus tháinig sé anoir agus ní thearn sé stad mara nó cónaí go raibh sé ag an Chrochaire Tharnocht.

"Buail buille sa tsealán agus lig anuas mé."

"Ní mé a chuir suas thú agus ní mé a ligfeas anuas thú," arsa Cormac.

Agus d'imigh sé agus an ceann leis agus d'fhág sé síos i gcúl teach an rí é agus chuaigh sé go dtí an doras.

"Tá dhá dtrian do níne bainte agam."

"Maith go leor," arsa an rí, "tá sí le fáil agat nuair a bheas sí bainte agat."

D'imigh Cormac agus chuaigh sé a luí an oíche sin. Agus níorbh fhada—má ba luath a d'éirigh an ghrian ní luaithe ná d'éirigh Cormac. Nigh sé a aghaidh agus a lámha agus chuir sé air a chulaith chatha agus a chrua chomhraic. Agus bhí scian ina láimh chlí agus

a chlaíomh síos siar leis. Ní thearn sé stad mara nó cónaí go raibh
sé ag an Chrochaire Tharnocht.

"Buail buille sa tsealán agus lig anuas mé."

"Ní mé a chuir suas thú agus ní mé a ligfeas anuas thú."

Níor stad sé go raibh sé ins an Domhan Thoir agus níorbh fhada
a bhí sé ansin gur mhoithigh sé, go bhfaca sé an fathach ag teacht.
Agus ba bheag ab fhiú an bheirt eile lena thaobh sin. Bhí an-mhéid
ann agus tífeá an domhan brách eadar a dhá chois agus ní fheicfeá
dadaí os cionn mhullach a chinn, bhí sé chomh hard sin.

"Cé acu is fearr leat greimeannaí caola cruaidhe coraíocht nó
*snap*annaí chlaíomh in easnacha a chéile?"

"Is fearr liom greimeannaí caola cruaidhe coraíocht. Is é a chleacht
mé i mbaile bheag, i mbaile mhór, i ngleann m'athara agus mo
mháthaire féin riamh."

Bhuail an dís lena chéile agus nuair a bhí neoin beag agus deireadh
an lae ann, chuir Cormac síos ar a ghlúin é. Tharraing sé air a
chlaíomh agus bhuail sé i gcomhrac a chinn agus a mhuinéil é agus
bhain sé an ceann de. D'imigh sé anoir agus an ceann leis go dtí go
raibh sé ag an Chrochaire Tharnocht.

"Buail—nuair a d'éirigh leat chomh maith agus d'éirigh," arsa
an Crochaire, "agus nach bhfeiceann tú féin nach bhfuil dadaí le—
le theacht ort—buail buille sa tsealán agus lig anuas mé."

Rinne Cormac amach gur mhór an trua an Crochaire agus bhuail
sé buille sa tsealán agus lig sé anuas an Crochaire Tarnocht. Rug
an Crochaire greim cúl cinn air agus ní raibh trom ar bith ann aige
ar dhóigh ar bith, agus chuir sé suas ins an tsealán é agus—ins an
tor. Agus bhí sé—bhí sé thuas ansin. Agus thug an Crochaire—thug
an Crochaire leis ceann an fhathaigh agus d'fhág sé síos go socair
suaimhneach i gcúl teach an rí é. Agus níor bhog sé plátaí ar an
drisiúir nó dadaí. Bhíodh na plátaí ag croitheadh ar an drisiúir nuair
a d'fhágfadh an fear eile síos an ceann. Ach níor bhog an Crochaire
dadaí. D'fhág sé síos go socair suaimhneach é agus chuaigh sé go dtí
an doras.

"Tá do níon bainte agam," arsa seisean.

Ó, bhuail brón an rí agus bhuail brón an níon. Agus chaithfeadh
sí a dhul leis ina dhiaidh sin. Agus rinneadh lá pósta agus pósadh
an Crochaire agus níon an rí. Agus ní raibh bainis ar bith ann a raibh
maith ar bith ann.

Agus bhí an Crochaire istigh sa choill. Ins an choill a bhí an teach. Agus achan mhaidin, nuair a d'éiríodh an crochaire, théadh sé amach fríd an choill ag seilg. Agus bhíodh sé ag ithe na n-éanacha fuara agus achan chineál beathach a bhfaigheadh sé a mharbhadh ins an choill. Agus bhí an-drochdhóigh ar níon an rí aige. Agus bhí sé mar sin sa choill ar feadh bliana. Agus bhí Cormac thuas ins an tsealán, cá bith an cineál sealáin a bhí sa chrann.

Agus bhí deartháir ag Cormac darbh ainm — *Pat.*

"Tá sé bliain agus an lá inniu," ar seisean, "ó d'imigh mo dheartháir. Agus ní bhfuair mé scolb nó scéala riamh ó shin air. Agus tá mise ag imeacht inniu," a deir sé, "go dtí go bhfeice mé caidé a d'éirigh dó."

Nigh sé a aghaidh agus a lámha agus chuir sé air a chulaith chatha agus a chrua chomhraic agus níor stad sé go dtí go raibh sé ag an Chrochaire Tharnocht. Nuair a d'amharc sé suas ar an Chrochaire, cé bhí thuas ach Cormac. Bhuail sé buille sa tsealán agus lig sé anuas Cormac. Agus nuair a fuair Cormac anuas, níor stop sé go dtí go raibh sé ag teach an rí. Agus phill[5] an fear eile abhaile. Agus —

"Tá mise ag dul," ar seisean, "go dtí go bhfeice mé an dtiocfadh liom an Crochaire Tarnocht a mharbhadh."

D'inis a bhean dó go raibh sé amuigh sa choill achan lá ag marbhadh éanacha fuara agus á n-ithe agus go raibh drochdhóigh uirthise. Agus dúirt sí nach dtiocfadh é a mharbhadh, nach raibh gar dó a bheith leis nó go raibh sé — go raibh sé láidir agus nach raibh gar a bheith leis.

"Cuma caidé mar tá sé," arsa Cormac, "*try*áilfidh mise ar ais an Crochaire go bhfeice mé é."

"Bhal, ná fan istigh," ar sise, "go dtige an Crochaire nó muirbhfidh an Crochaire thusa má — má thig sé agus tú istigh."

D'imigh Cormac agus tháinig an Crochaire. Agus nuair a tháinig sé isteach —

"Hó, hó," a deir sé leis an bhean, "tá boladh an Éireannaigh bhréagaigh fá do theach."

"Ó, maise, níl," a deir sí, "boladh ar bith den tseort fá mo theachsa ar chor ar bith a dtearnadh riamh," a deir sí. "Agus ní ligfidh mise thusa chun na coille," a deir sí, "an darna lá le heagla — bím ag *fret*áil achan lá fá dtaobh duit — le heagla go muirbhfí thú, nó go dtiocfadh dadaí ort. Agus ní ligfidh mé chun na coille níos mó thú. Caithfidh tú fuireacht istigh feasta."

"Ná bíodh buaireamh ar bith ort fá dtaobh domhsa, nó ní—ní thiocfadh mise a mharbhadh," arsa—arsa an Crochaire, "nó ní mhuirfidhear choíche mise go dtí go ngearrfar an crann atá thoir ag tóin teach mo dhearthára sa Domhan Thoir, agus go bhfaghfar an tseantua bhriste bhearnach atá faoi cholbha a leapa, go ngearrfar an crann mór atá ag tóin an tí. Agus éireochaidh gearria amach as an chrann agus imeochaidh sé agus go dtí go bhfaighfear Cú Glas na Coille Léithe go dtí go mbeire sí ar an ghearria; agus imeochaidh seabhac amach as tóin an ghearria agus imeochaidh sé suas ar eiteoig ins an spéir; agus go bhfaghfar Seabhac Ghleann Dá Mhaol é, go dtí go mbuailfidh sé *dab* ar an tseabhac go leagfaidh sé anuas é; agus titfidh uibh amach as tóin an tseabhaic síos ar thóin na haibhléise; agus go dtí go bhfaghfar Faoileog Cheann Trá go dtóga sí an uibh;[6] agus go dtuga sí duit i gcúlaibh do dhoirn í agus go mbuailfear ins an bhall odhráin atá ar mo bhrollach mise," arsa an Crochaire, "ní thiocfadh mise a mharbhadh."

"Ó, bhal, más mar sin mar atá," ar sise, "thig leat a dhul chun na coille am ar bith ar mian leat agus ní bheidh *fret* ar bith ormsa."

D'imigh an Crochaire bocht chun na coille. Agus bhí sé ins an choill ag seilg. Agus chuaigh Cormac soir agus fuair sé an tseantua bhriste bhearnach a bhí faoi cholbha leapa na bhfathaigh a bhí thoir. Agus bhuail sé trí bhuille ar bhun an chrainn agus thit an crann. Léim an gearria amach as faoi bhun an chrainn agus scairt sé—

"Cú Glas na Coille Léithe le comhair anseo!"

Ní raibh an focal as a bhéal go raibh Cú Glas na Coille Léithe i ndiaidh an ghearria agus fuair sí *hold*[7] air. D'imigh éan amach as tóin an ghearria agus d'imigh sé suas os cionn na farraige. Agus thit—

"Seabhac Ghleann Dá Mhaol anseo," ar seisean, "ar an bhomaite le comhair!"

Ní raibh an focal as a bhéal go raibh Seabhac Ghleann Dá Mhaol aige. Agus bhuail sé *dab* anuas ar dhroim an éin agus thit uibh síos ar thóin na haibhléise. Agus—

"Faoileog Cheann Trá anseo le comhair!" ar seisean.

Ní raibh an focal as a bhéal go raibh Faoileog Cheann Trá aige agus thóg sí an uibh agus thug sí dó i gcúl a dhoirn í.

Agus tháinig Cormac anoir agus an uibh leis. Agus tháinig sé go teach an fhathaigh. Agus ní raibh an fathach istigh — bhí sé sa choill. Agus d'iarr a bhean air gan a dhul á chóir nó go muirbhfeadh sé cinnte é. Dúirt Cormac go d*try*áilfeadh sé ar scor ar bith.

Nuair a bhí sé — d'imigh sé síos faoin teach agus nuair a bhí sé ag dul síos faoin teach, bhí an fathach chuige aníos agus a bhrollach foscailte síos siar aige. Agus d'fhan Cormac riamh go raibh sé chóir a bheith aige agus bhuail sé an uibh ins an bhrollach ar an fhathach. Agus thit an fathach marbh.

Agus chuaigh Cormac chun an tí ansin. Agus pósadh Cormac agus níon an rí. Agus bhí naoi n-oíche agus naoi lá bainse ann agus tá siad go maith ón lá sin go dtí an lá inniu.
SÓC   Maith thú!

19

HUNG-UP NAKED

Once upon a time, there was a king and he had a daughter and she was to be got by any man who would kill three giants that were in the Eastern World and bring back their heads and deposit them nice and quietly at his house.

There was a man called Prince Cormac of *Ealla*. Cormac got up one morning and put on his battle and hard combat dress. He had his knife in his left hand and his sword by his side and he made no sea-halt or delay till he reached Hung-Up Naked.

"Strike a blow against the noose," says Hung-Up, "and let me down," says the —

"By my oath," says he, "it wasn't I who hoisted you and it isn't I who'll cut you down."

Cormac carried on and never halted till he reached the Eastern World. He wasn't long there till he heard the bellowing giant coming. This big giant came and you could see the whole world between his two legs and nothing above his head, he was so tall. Cormac and he met up and after they had fought a while. —

"Do not kill me altogether, foolish young warrior," said he, "and I'll give you the old broken, jagged axe which is under my bed."

"That will be mine," says Cormac, "after your day."

Cormac struck him a blow where his head and neck met and cut off his head. He took the head with him and brought it back and came as far as Hung-Up Naked. Hung-Up was up in the bush with no way of coming down.

"Strike a blow against the noose, since you did so well," said he, "and cut me down."

"It is not I who hoisted you and it is not I who'll cut you down," says Cormac.

Cormac went to the rear of the king's palace and deposited the giant's head nice and quietly there and he went up to the door.

"I have won one third of your daughter," said he to the king.

"Fair enough," said the king.

Cormac went home and went to bed that night. No sooner did the day dawn than did Cormac arise. He washed his face and hands, donned his battle- and hard combat dress and he had his knife in his left hand and his sword by his side. And he made neither sea-halt or delay till he reached Hung-Up Naked.

"Strike a blow against the noose," says Hung-Up, "and cut me down."

"It is not I who hoisted you and it is not I who'll cut you down."

He made no sea-halt or delay till he was with the giants in the Eastern World. He wasn't long there till he heard the giant coming. When the giant came up to him —

"You killed my brother yesterday," said he, "but you won't succeed today," says he. "I'll put an end to you today. Which do you prefer, wrestling holds, dire and tough or hewing with swords at each other's ribs?"

"I prefer wrestling holds, dire and tough," says Cormac. "Such I know of old and practised in town and village and in my father's and mother's glen."

The two engaged and when evening and day's end came, Cormac brought him to his knees. He raised his sword and struck him where his head and neck met and cut off his head.

He took the head back with him and made no sea-halt or delay till he reached Hung-Up Naked.

"Strike a blow against the noose and cut me down."

"It is not I who hoisted you and it is not I who'll cut you down," says Cormac.

On he went with the head and deposited it behind the king's palace and he went up to the door.

"I have won two-thirds of your daughter."

"Fair enough," says the king, "You shall have her when you win her."

Cormac went away to bed that night. And it wasn't long, however early the sun arose, Cormac arose just as early. He washed his face and hands and donned his battle and hard combat dress. He had a knife in his left hand and his sword by his side and he made no sea-halt or delay till he came to Hung-Up Naked.

"Strike a blow against the noose and cut me down."

"It is not I who hoisted you and it is not I who'll cut you down."

He never halted till he reached the Eastern World and he wasn't long there till he heard, he saw the giant coming. The other two weren't worth much by comparison. He was huge and you could see the whole world between his two legs and you could see nothing over his head, he was so tall.

"Which do you prefer, wrestling holds, dire and tough or hewing with swords at each other's ribs?"

"I prefer wrestling holds, dire and tough. Such I know of old and practised in town and village and in my father's and mother's glen."

The two engaged and when evening and day's end came, Cormac brought him to his knees. He raised his sword and struck him where his head and neck met and cut off his head. He returned with the head then and came up to Hung-Up Naked.

"Strike — since you did so well," says Hung-Up Naked, "strike a blow against the noose and cut me down."

Cormac thought a great pity of Hung-Up Naked and he struck a blow against the noose and cut down Hung-Up Naked. Without the slightest effort, Hung-Up Naked caught him by the back of the neck and hoisted him in the noose, up in the bush. And there he was up there. So, Hung-Up took the giant's head with him and deposited it nice and quietly at the back of the king's palace. He never moved a plate on the dresser or anything. The plates shook on the dresser when the other man left the head down. But Hung-Up didn't

move anything. He left it down nice and quietly and he went up to
the door.

"I have won your daughter," said he.

Oh, the king was distraught and so was his daughter. And there
was nothing — she had to — she had to go with him after that. And
a wedding day was appointed and Hung-Up and the king's daughter
were married. And the wedding wasn't up to much.

So, Hung-Up was in the wood. That's where the house was. Every
morning when Hung-Up got up, he would head off hunting in the
wood. He used to eat birds raw and every kind of creature he managed
to kill in the wood. He had the king's daughter reduced to a very
sad state. He was there in the wood for a whole year. And Cormac
was hanging in the noose, whatever sort of noose was in the tree.

So, Cormac had a brother called Pat.

"It's a year and a day, this day," said he, "since my brother went
away. And tale nor tidings of him have I had since. So, I'm heading
off today," says he, "to see what happened to him."

He washed his face and hands and donned his battle and hard
combat dress and he never halted till he reached Hung-Up Naked.
When he looked up at Hung-Up, who was it only Cormac. He struck
a blow against the noose and cut Cormac down. When Cormac came
down, he never halted until he reached the king's palace. The other
fellow returned home.

"I am going to see if I could kill Hung-Up Naked," said he.

His wife told him he was out in the wood every day killing birds
and eating them raw and that she was in a bad way. And she said
he couldn't be killed, that there was no point in trying, that he was
strong and it was no use.

"It doesn't matter how he may be," said Cormac, "I'll have a go
at Hung-Up again just to see."

"Well, don't stay in," says she, "till Hung-Up comes, or he'll kill
you if he comes and finds you inside."

Cormac went off and — he didn't stay inside. Hung-Up arrived.
And when he came in —

"Ho, ho," says he to his wife, "there's the smell of a thieving
Irishman in your house."

"Oh, indeed, there isn't," says she, "a smell of the sort in my house
or never was," says she. "And I won't allow you to go to the wood

again for fear — I worry about you every day — for fear that you'd be killed, or something happen to you. And I won't allow you to go to the wood any more. You'll have to remain at home in future.

"Oh well, I won't stay — don't worry about me, for I couldn't be killed," says Hung-Up, "for I shall never be killed until the tree that is growing by my brother's house in the Eastern World is cut down, and until the old broken jagged saw that's under his bed is got to cut the tree that's at his house. And a hare will rise up out of the tree and head away and until The Grey Hound of *Coill Liath* is got to catch the hare; and a hawk will fly out of the hare's arse and wing it up in the air; and until The Hawk of *Gleann Dá Mhaol* is got and pecks the hawk and forces it down; and an egg will fall out of the hawk down to the bottom of the ocean; and until The Seagull of *Ceann Trá* is got to find the egg; and until it gives it to you in your fist and until I am struck on the mole on my breast," says Hung-Up, "I could not be killed."

"Oh well, if that's the way," says she, "you can go to the wood any time you like and I won't fret one bit."

Poor Hung-Up went off to the wood. And he was hunting in the wood. Cormac headed off east and he got the old broken jagged axe that was under the eastern giant's bed. And he struck three blows at the bottom of the tree and it fell. The hare jumped out from under the tree and he shouted —

"The Grey Hound of *Coill Liath* here to my aid!"

No sooner had he said the word than the Grey Hound of *Coill Liath* was after the hare and she caught it. A bird flew out of the hare's arse and soared up over the sea. And out fell —

"The Hawk of *Gleann Dá Mhaol* here immediately to my aid!"

No sooner had he said the word than he had The Hawk of *Gleann Dá Mhaol* there and it pecked at the bird's back and an egg fell down to the bottom of the ocean. And —

"The Seagull of *Ceann Trá* here to my aid!" says he.

No sooner had he said the word than he had The Seagull of *Ceann Trá* there and he fetched the egg from the bottom of the ocean and placed it in the hollow of his hand.

So, Cormac came back with the egg. And he arrived at the giant's house. And the giant wasn't at home — he was in the wood. And his wife begged him not to go near him, saying that he would kill him for sure. Cormac said that he would give it a try anyway.

When he was—he went off down below the house and as he was going down, he met the giant coming up and bare to the waist. Cormac bided his time until he was almost on top of him and then he struck the giant's breast with the egg. And the giant fell down dead.

So, Cormac went up to the house. And Cormac and the king's daughter were married. And the wedding feast lasted nine days and nine nights and they are the best from that day to this.

This recording was made on 26.12.1973. Duration 11' 15". Tape 85/1 and 2 SÓC (9 cms.p.s.).

CONALL EOGHAIN PHÁDRAIG MAC AN LUAIN

AN TOIRTÍN BEAG AGUS AN TOIRTÍN MÓR

Bhí bean ann i bhfad ó shin agus bhí triúr níonach aici. Bhí sí ina baintrigh agus ní raibh aici ach triúr na níonach. Agus dúirt bean acu lá amháin go raibh sise ag dul ar a saothrú. Rinne sí réidh agus d'imigh sí agus rinne an chailleach toirtín beag agus toirtín mór agus thug sí díthi iad.

"Cé acu is fearr leat an toirtín mór is mo mhallacht," ar sise, "nó an toirtín beag is mo bheannacht?"

"Is fearr liom an toirtín mór agus do mhallacht," arsa an cailín.

Thug sí an toirtín mór díthi agus chuaigh sí suas i mullach claí agus bhí sí ag mallachtaigh i mullach an chlaí gur thit an claí faoina dhá cois.

Agus d'imigh an cailín agus an toirtín mór léithi agus a mallacht. Agus shiúil sí léithi agus chuaigh sí isteach i—tharlaigh isteach i dteach go deireanach í agus ní raibh ann ach cailleach amháin, ins an teach. D'fhiafraigh an chailleach díthi cá raibh sí ag dul agus dúirt sí go raibh sí ag dul ar a saothrú.

"Fostóchaidh mise thú," ar sise, "bliain agus lá. Agus ní bheidh dadaí agat le déanamh ach trí ribe ghlas atá i mo cheann a choinneáil pioctha agus gan amharc suas ins an tsimiléir!

D'fhostóigh an chailleach í agus rinne sí fostó léithi bliain agus lá agus gan dadaí le déanamh aici ach na trí ribe ghlas a phiocadh as ceann na caillí agus gan amharc suas ins an tsimiléir.

Bhí sí ag piocadh léithi ar cheann na caillí achan lá agus, lá amháin, thit an chailleach ina codladh agus í ag piocadh ar na rudaí a bhí ina ceann. Agus d'amharc an cailín suas ins an tsimiléir agus thit mála óir agus mála airgid anuas as an tsimiléir.

Thóg an cailín é agus d'imigh sí agus é léithi. Chuaigh sí fhad leis an tseanghearrán bhán—bhí seanghearrán bán ar téad ann—agus chuaigh sí fhad leis an tseanghearrán bhán.

"Athraigh mé, athraigh mé," ar seisean, "níor hathraíodh le seacht mbliana mé."

"Ní athróchaidh," ar sise, "níl faill agam."

D'imigh sí léithi agus chuaigh sí fhad le claí a bhí ann.

"Caith méaróg orm agus ceann díom," arsa an claí. Níor hathraíodh le seacht mbliana mé."

"Níl faill agam," ar sise.

Shiúil sí léithi ansin. D'imigh sí léithi ansin an méid a bhí ina corp agus tháinig sí abhaile. Agus ní raibh sí i bhfad—ní raibh sí—ní raibh baol uirthi a bheith sa bhaile go dtí gur mhúscail an chailleach. Agus bhí slaitín draíochta ag an chailligh agus tharraing sí uirthi é agus d'imigh sí ina diaidh. Chuaigh sí fhad leis an tseanghearrán bhán.

"Ar mhoithigh tú cailín ar bith ag dul thart," ar sise, "ar ball, lena, le mo *jig-jag* agus le mo *wig-wag*, le mo dhá mhála óir agus airgid agus an méid a shaothraigh mé ó baisteadh mé?"

"Chuaigh sí thart ansin ar ball," arsa an seanghearrán bán.

D'imigh sí léithi ansin agus chuaigh sí fhad leis an chlaí.

"Ar mhoithigh tú cailín ar bith ag dul thart ansin ar ball le mo *jig-jag* agus le mo *wig-wag*, le mo dhá mhála óir agus airgid agus an méid a shaothraigh mé ó baisteadh mé?"

"Chuaigh sí thart ansin ar ball," ar seisean.

D'imigh an chailleach ina diaidh agus fuair an chailleach *hold* uirthi sula raibh sí sa bhaile. Bhuail sí trí bhuille den tslaitín draíochta uirthi agus rinne sí cnap cloiche díthi. Thug sí léithi a dhá mhála óir agus airgid agus chuaigh sí abhaile ar ais, an chailleach.

Agus nuair a bhí bliain agus lá istigh, dúirt bean eile de na cailíní go raibh sise ag imeacht inniu ar a saothrú, gur imigh an bhean eile bliain agus an lá inniu agus go n-imeochadh sise inniu, nach bhfuair siad scéala ar bith fá dtaobh díthi ó shin. D'éirigh an chailleach agus rinne sí dhá thoirtín, toirtín beag agus toirtín mór.

"Cé acu is fearr leat an toirtín mór is mo mhallacht nó an toirtín beag is mo bheannacht?"

"Is fearr liom an toirtín mór is do mhallacht."

Chuaigh an chailleach suas ar an chlaí agus bhí sí ag mallachtaigh go raibh an claí ag titim faoina dhá cois. Agus d'imigh an cailín agus an toirtín.

Níor stad sí go raibh sí ag an chailligh chéanna. Agus d'fhostóigh an chailleach í bliain agus lá agus gan dadaí aici le déanamh ach na trí ribe ghlas a bhí ina ceann a choinneáil pioctha agus gan amharc suas ins an tsimiléir.

Gorra, lá amháin, thit an chailleach ina codladh agus d'amharc sí suas ins an tsimiléir agus thit mála óir agus mála airgid anuas. D'imigh an cailín agus sin léithi. Agus chuaigh sí fhad leis an tseanghearrán bhán.

"Athraigh mé, athraigh mé, níor hathraíodh le seacht mbliana mé."

"Ní athróchaidh, maise," a deir sí, "nó níl faill agam."

D'imigh sí léithi agus chuaigh sí fhad leis an chlaí.

"Athraigh mé, athraigh mé, níor hathraíodh le seacht mbliana mé."

"Ní athróchaidh," ar sise, "níl faill agam."

Mhúscail an chailleach agus d'imigh sí ina diaidh agus a slaitín draíochta. Agus ní theachaidh sí i bhfad uilig go dtí go bhfuair an chailleach fhad léithi agus bhuail sí trí bhuille uirthi agus rinne sí cnapán cloiche díthi. Agus phill sí abhaile ar ais agus a mála óir agus airgid léithi. Agus—

"Tá bliain agus lá," ar sise—"tá dhá bhliain agus dhá lá," arsa an cailín deireanach, "ó d'imigh an chéad bhean de mo chuid deirfiúracha. Agus tá sé bliain agus lá ó d'imigh an bhean eile. Agus tá an t-am agamsa imeacht inniu go bhfeice mé caidé d'éirigh díofa nuair nach bhfuair muid scéala ar bith ó shin uathu."

D'imigh an cailín deireanach ansin. D'éirigh an chailleach agus rinne sí toirtín díthi. Rinne sí dhá thoirtín.

"Cé acu is fearr leat an toirtín mór is mo mhallacht nó an toirtín beag is mo bheannacht?"

"Is fearr liom an toirtín beag is do bheannacht," arsa an—arsa an ceann deireanach.

Shiúil sí léithi ansin. Agus níor stad sí go raibh sí ag an chailligh chéanna. D'fhostóigh an chailleach í bliain agus lá. Agus ní raibh dadaí aici le déanamh ach na trí ribe ghlas a phiocadh as a ceann agus gan amharc suas ins an tsimiléir.

Bhí sí ag piocadh ar cheann na caillí agus thit an chailleach, lá amháin, ina codladh. Agus d'amharc sí suas ins an tsimiléir. Thit mála óir agus mála airgid anuas as an tsimiléir. Agus thóg sí é agus thug sí léithi é. Agus d'amharc sí thart agus fuair sí slaitín draíochta na caillí agus thug sí léithi í.

Mhúscail an—chuaigh sí fhad leis an tseanghearrán bhán.

G

"Athraigh mé, athraigh mé," ar seisean, "níor hathraíodh le seacht mbliana mé."

"Seo anois, ní bheidh mé i bhfad á dhéanamh sin," ar sise.

Chaith sí uaithi deireadh agus d'athraigh sí an seanghearrán bán ar fhéar mhaith. Agus d'imigh sí léithi ansin agus chuaigh sí fhad leis an chlaí.

"Caith cloch bheag orm agus ceann díom. Níor hathraíodh le seacht mbliana mé," arsa an claí.

"Ní bheidh mé i bhfad á dhéanamh sin," ar sise.

Chaith sí méaróg ar an chlaí agus ceann de. Chuir sí athrú mar sin air. Agus d'imigh sí léithi ar ais agus an rud léithi uilig go léir. Agus ní raibh sé i bhfad go dtáinig an chailleach. Mhúscail an chailleach agus lean sí í. Agus ní raibh slaitín draíochta ar bith aici, ag an chailligh. Agus tháinig sí fhad leis an tseanghearrán bhán.

"Ar mhoithigh tú cailín ar bith ag dul thart ansin ar ball, le mo jig-jag agus le mo wig-wag, le mo dhá mhála óir agus airgid agus an méid a shaothraigh mé ó baisteadh mé?"

Thúsaigh an seanghearrán bán uirthi á ciceáil agus ar achan dóigh a bhfaigheadh sé fhad léithi. Hobair go muirbhfeadh sé an chailleach.

D'imigh an chailleach agus chuaigh sí fhad leis an chlaí. Agus d'fhiafraigh sí den chlaí ar mhoithigh sé cailín ar bith ag dul thart ansin ar ball—"le mo jig-jag agus le mo wig-wag, le mo dhá mhála óir agus airgid agus an méid a shaothraigh mé ó baisteadh mé?"

"Chuaigh sí thart," ar seisean—ní hea, thúsaigh an claí uirthi ag caitheamh cloch uirthi. Agus hobair nach bhfaighfeadh sí ar shiúl.

D'imigh an chailleach léithi agus b'éigean don chailligh a dhul ar fad. Bhí an slaitín draíochta na caillí leis an cheann óg agus bhuail sí buille ar achan bhean de na deirfiúracha agus chuir sí ina seasamh iad.

Agus chuaigh an triúr cailín abhaile agus bhí an triúr sa bhaile.

Agus tháinig an chailleach. D'éirigh sí amach leis an tslaitín draíochta agus bhuail sí trí bhuille ar an chailligh agus rinne sí cnapán cloiche díthi.

Agus, tá siad go maith ón lá sin go dtí an lá inniu.

20

THE LITTLE SCONE AND THE BIG ONE

Long ago there was a woman who had three daughters. She was a widow and she only had the three daughters. So, one day, one of them said she was off to earn a living. She got ready and away she went and the old woman made a little scone and a big one and she gave them to her.

"Which would you rather have," said she, "the big scone and my ʼurse or the little scone and my blessing?"

"I prefer the big scone and your curse," says the girl.

She gave her the big scone and she got up on top of the ditch and she cursed on top of the ditch until the ditch fell from under her two feet.

So, the girl headed off with the big scone and the curse. She walked on and she went—finally, she happened into a house and the only one in the house was an old woman. The old woman asked her where she was going and she said she was going off to earn her living.

"I'll hire you," said she, "for a year and a day. And the only thing you'll have to do is to keep three grey hairs in my head picked and not to look up the chimney."

The girl agreed to hire for a year and a day and the old woman hired her, her only work being to pick the three grey hairs from the old woman's head and not to look up the chimney.

There she was picking the old woman's head every day and, one day, the old woman fell asleep while she was picking. So, the girl looked up the chimney and down fell a bag of gold and a bag of silver out of the chimney.

The girl lifted it and away she went. She went as far as the old grey horse—there was an old grey horse tethered there—and she went as far as it.

"Move me, move me," said he, "I haven't been moved this seven years."

"Indeed, I won't," said she, "I haven't time."

Off she went till she came to a ditch there.

"Throw a pebble on me and take one off me," says the ditch. "I haven't been altered for seven years."

"I haven't time," said she.

She walked on and she went as hard as she could till she got home. It wasn't long — she wasn't near home when the old woman woke up. The old woman had a magic wand and she grabbed it and headed off after her. She came to the old grey horse.

"Did you notice a girl going by," said she, "a while ago, with my jig-jag and my wig-wag with my two bags of gold and silver and everything I earned since my baptism?"

"She passed by a while ago," says the old grey horse.

On she went till she came to the ditch.

"Did you notice a girl going by a while ago with my jig-jag and my wig-wag, with my two bags of gold and silver and all I earned since my baptism?"

"She passed by a while ago," says he.

The old woman continued in pursuit and she got hold of her before she reached home. She gave her three blows of her magic wand and she turned her to stone. The old woman took the two bags of gold and silver home with her.

When the year and a day was up, another of the girls said that she was going to earn her living that very day, that the other girl had left a year and a day before that and that she was going today for she hadn't heard any news of her since then. The old woman got up and made two scones, a little one and a big one.

"Which do you prefer, the big scone and my curse or the little scone and my blessing?"

"I prefer the big scone and your curse."

The old woman got up on the ditch and she was cursing on the ditch until it began to collapse under her feet. So, the girl went off with her scone.

She never halted till she came to the same old woman. And the old woman hired her for a year and a day with nothing to do but keep the three grey hairs in her head picked and not to look up the chimney.

Well, one day, the old woman fell asleep and she looked up the chimney and down fell a bag of gold and a bag of silver. And away the girl went with them. So, she came to the old grey horse.

"Move me, move me, I haven't been moved for seven years."

"Indeed, I won't," says she, "I haven't time."

The old woman woke up and off she went after her with her magic wand. And she hadn't gone very far before the old woman caught up with her and gave her three blows (of the wand) and turned her to stone. She came back then with her bag of gold and bag of silver.

"It's a year and a day," says she — "it's two years and two days," says the last of the girls, "since the first of my sisters left. And it's a year and a day since the second one left. And it's time for me to be leaving today to see what has happened to them since we have heard nothing from them."

The last of the girls left then. The old woman got up and she made her a scone. She made two scones.

"Which would you rather have, the big scone and my curse or the little scone and my blessing?"

"I prefer the little scone and your blessing," says the last of the girls.

Off she went then and she never halted till she reached the same old woman. The old woman hired her for a year and a day, her only work being to keep the three grey hairs picked in the old woman's head and not to look up the chimney.

She was picking the old woman's head one day and she fell asleep. So, she looked up the chimney. Down fell a bag of gold and a bag of silver out of the chimney. So, she lifted it and took it with her. She took a look around and she found the old woman's magic wand and she took it with her too.

She came to the old grey horse.

"Move me, move me," says he, "I haven't been moved for seven years."

"Well, I won't be long doing that," says she.

She left everything down and she moved the old grey horse to good grazing. Then she went on as far as the ditch.

"Throw a stone on me and take one away. I haven't been altered for seven years," says the ditch.

"I won't be long doing that," says she.

She threw a pebble on the ditch and took one off it and altered it thus. Off she went again and everything with her. So, it wasn't long till the old woman came. She woke up and followed her. The old woman had no magic wand and she came to the old white horse.

"Did you notice a girl going by," says she, "a while ago, with my jig-jag and my wig-wag, my two bags of gold and silver and all I earned since my baptism?"

The old white horse started on her, kicking her and everything he could do. He nearly killed the old woman.

The old woman went on till she came to the ditch. She asked the ditch if he had noticed a girl going by a while before that—"with my jig-jag and wig-wag, my two bags of gold and silver and everything I earned since I was baptised?"

"She went by," said he—no, the ditch started on her, throwing stones at her and she very nearly didn't get away.

On the old woman went and she was forced to go the whole way. The young woman had the old woman's magic wand and she gave each of the sisters a blow and restored them.

So, the three girls went home and there they were. The old woman arrived. Out she went with her magic wand and gave her three blows of it and turned her to stone.

And they're the best from that day to this.

This recording was made on 26.12.1973. Duration 7' 05". Tape 85/2 SÓC (9 cms.p.s.).

21

GOLL MAC MORNA

Bhal, fad ó shin, nuair a bhí na Fiannaibh[1] in Éirinn, bhí siad ina gcónaí thiar i nGleann Cholm Cille. Agus bhí an—bhí an-foirgneamh[2] tithe acu ann. Agus bhí siad ag seilg aniar Gleann na nGleanntach—is é an t-ainm a bhéaradh siad ar Ghleann na nGleanntach, Gleann Fada na Sealg.

Bhí lá amháin, agus bhí siad ag imeacht aniar Gleann na nGleanntach a sheilg agus ní rachadh Goll leofa. Bhí sé ina luí istigh is—i leaba a bhí aige, agus ní rachadh sé leofa aniar an Gleann ar chor ar bith a sheilg.

Agus d'imigh an chuid eile acu aniar an Gleann a sheilg. Nuair a bhí siad aniar i lár an Ghleanna, dhruid sé isteach i gceo agus thoisigh ceobrán. Bhí Fionn Mac Cumhaill leofa agus chuir sé a ordóg ina bhéal agus rinne sé seort cognadh uirthi agus rinne sé fios. Dúirt sé gur sin ceo coscartha cuir agus tithe á loscadh ar dhaoine.

Bhí Goll thiar agus bhí sé ina chodladh agus ní mhúsclóchadh dadaí é ach rud a dtugadh siad conairteacha air. Bhí na mná uilig thiar—d'fhág siad na mná ina ndiaidh ins an bhaile—agus rinne na mná amach go dtabharfadh siad *trick* do Gholl nuair nach dtiocfadh sé aniar a sheilg.

Cheangail siad cuid gruaige Gholl thuas ar na creataí uilig go léir. Bhí gruag mhór fhada air agus cheangail siad an ghruag uilig go léir thuas ar na creataí nuair a bhí Goll ina chodladh. Agus chuaigh siad amach ansin agus na madaidh leofa a dhéanamh conairteacha.

Nuair a thoisigh na conairteacha amuigh—cá bith an rud na conairteacha—mhúscail Goll agus d'éirigh sé in airde istigh sa leaba agus d'fhág sé craiceann a chinn ar na creataí—bhí a ghruag ceangailte.

Chuaigh sé amach. Agus bhí na mná amuigh. Agus bhí oiread—bhí oiread feirge air agus bhí sé scriosta mar bhí sé féin agus chruinnigh sé suas carnán mór brosnaí—bhal, b'fhéidir go raibh toirt tí ann—agus chuir sé le thine é agus rug sé ar na mná uilig go léir agus chaith sé isteach ann iad. Agus dhóigh sé deireadh na mban. Níor fhág sé bean beo acu.

Agus tháinig na fir a bhí ag seilg agus d'imigh Goll. Agus chuaigh sé amach thíos ar carraig, an áit a dtugann siad Carraig Ghoill uirthi. Síos fá na Rosa atá sí. Níl fhios agamsa cá háit ina bhfuil sí, ach tá sí thíos ar scor ar bith, Carraig Ghoill. Agus bhí sé amuigh ar an charraig. Tá sí amach giota san fharraige. Agus lean siad go dtí an bruach é agus ní raibh aon duine acu ábalta a dhul amach. Agus bhí siad ina seasamh, chuir siad ansin na saighdiúirí a bhí acu á choimheád taobh amuigh. Agus bhí Goll ar an charraig agus na saighdiúirí taobh amuigh agus ní thiocfadh leis a theacht amach.

Agus nuair a bhí sé naoi n-oíche agus naoi lá istigh ar an charraig, chaith siad isteach ceathrú de mhart chuige. D'éirigh Goll ina sheasamh amuigh ar an charraig agus chaith sé isteach an cheathrú agus mharbhaigh sé naoi naonúir[3] acu leis an cheathrú a chaith sé isteach.

"Tá mise anseo," ar seisean, "le naoi n-oíche agus naoi lá,
Ag sileadh gruaidhe agus ag ól sáile,
Rud nach raibh aon fhear romham riamh
Agus nach mbíonn i mo dhiaidh."
Sílim gur sin deireadh de.

SÓC   Cé aige ar mhoithigh tú an scéal sin, a Phádraig?

Ag seanbhean a bhí thoir ansin, maise, Róise. An bhean a bhí ag—ag—ag Eoghan Mhicheáil a bhí thoir ansin. Tá sí marbh le fada.

SÓC   An raibh mórán scéalta aici?

Bhí mórán scéalta aici cinnte, bhí.

SÓC   An bhfuil sé i bhfad ó shin ó mhoithigh tú é?

Arú, is fada an t-am é, is fada. Tá sé dhaichead bliain ó chuala mé é.

21

GOLL MAC MORNA

Well, long ago , when the *Fianna* were in Ireland, they were living back in Glencolmcille. And they had a big settlement of houses there. And they hunted the Glen of Glenties—the name they gave it was The Long Glen of the Hunt.

One day when they were leaving Glencolmcille to hunt, Goll wouldn't go with them. He was lying inside on his bed and he wouldn't go with them to hunt up the Glen at all.

So, the others left to go hunting up the Glen. When they were up the middle of the Glen, rain and mist closed in around them. Fionn Mac Cumhaill was with them and he put his thumb in his mouth and chewed it a bit and he was able to discern that there was a withering mist of rain and that people's houses were being burned.

Goll was at home sleeping and nothing could wake him except something they call 'conairteacha'. The women were all there—they left all the women at home—and they decided that they would play a trick on Goll since he wouldn't join the hunt.

They tied Goll's hair up all round the rafters. He had great long hair and they tied it all up on the rafters when Goll was asleep. Then they went out with the dogs to make 'conairteacha'.

When the conairteacha began outside—whatever they can be—Goll awoke and stood up in the bed and he left his scalp on the rafters; his hair was tied.

He went out. The women were outside. He was so angry and in such a shape, destroyed, that he gathered up a pile of sticks, maybe as big as a house, and he set fire to it and he caught hold of all the women and he flung them into it. And he burned the lot of them. He didn't leave one of them alive.

So, the men who were hunting came back and Goll made off. He went out onto a rock they call Goll's Rock. It's down about the Rosses. I don't know exactly where it is, but it's down about the Rosses anyway. And he was out on the rock. It's out a bit in the sea and they followed him to the edge but none of them was able to go out. While they were standing there, they had their soldiers on guard all round. And Goll was on the rock and the soldiers on the shore and he couldn't escape.

When he had spent nine days and nine nights on the rock, they threw a quarter of beef out to him. Goll stood up on the rock and he cast the quarter of beef back in and he killed nine times nine of them with the quarter of beef that he threw in.

"I have been here," says he, "for nine nights and nine days,
Drinking brine with weeping countenance,
What no man has ever done

Before or will after."

I think that's all.

SÓC   Who did you hear tell that story, Pádraig?

An old woman over there, Róise. Eoghan Mhicheáil's wife over there. She's dead a long time.

SÓC   Did she know many stories?

She did surely, she did.

SÓC   How long is it since you heard it?

Oh, it's a long, long time. It's forty years since I heard it.

This recording was made on 19.7.1972. Duration 3' 46". Tape 25/1 SÓC (9 cms.p.s.).

CONALL EOGHAIN PHÁDRAIG MAC AN LUAIN—"Conall an Damhsa"

22

AN FEARGHAMHAIN

Bhal, bhí an Fearghamhain, bhí sé ina chónaí thiar i nGleann Cholm Cille. Agus rinne sé amach—bhí deirfiúr dó amuigh ansin fá Fhiontún—agus rinne sé amach go dtiocfadh sé aniar lá amháin go dtí go bhfeicfeadh sé an deirfiúr.

Nuair a bhí sé ag fágáil thiar—bhí muc thiar ansin an áit a dtugann siad Malach na Muice air, ar an Ghleann Mhór, agus ní raibh aon duine a dtiocfadh a chóir an áit a raibh sí ann, a raibh an soipín aici, nach muirbhfeadh sí—agus nuair a bhí sé ag fágáil thiar, chros siad air a dhul bealach na muice.

"Is maith a bhí fhios agaibh," ar seisean, "nuair a chrosfadh sibh sin ormsa, go gcaithfinn a dhéanamh."

D'imigh an Fearghamhain agus bhí bata leis. Agus tháinig sé aniar an Gleann. Agus chuaigh sé fhad—nuair a chuaigh sé fhad leis an tsoipín a bhí ag an mhuic—bhí dhá bhanbhán[1] aici—lasc[2] sé a bhata istigh. Mharbh sé an dá bhanbhán agus d'fhág[3] sé a bhata istigh ins an tsoipín agus shiúil sé leis.

Agus bhí trí madaidh leis, madadh a raibh Loinseachán air agus Grathaigh agus Griobaigh. Agus d'imigh sé leis ansin agus nuair a bhí sé tamall beag ar shiúl, tháinig an mhuc agus bhí na banbháin marbh agus bhí an fear ar shiúl.

Chuir an mhuc boladh an fhir agus lean sí é. Agus nuair a bhí sé ag dul suas—nuair a bhí sé ag dul suas—ó, Bullaigh[4]—nuair a bhí sé ag dul suas an Mhullaigh, scaoil, tháinig sí fhad leis agus scaoil sé Bullaigh léithi. D'imigh sé an méid a bhí ina chorp ansin agus mharbh an mhuc Bullaigh agus lean sí ar ais é.

Agus nuair a bhí sé ag dul amach Srath Loinsigh, scaoil sé Loinseachán léithi—chuaigh sí fhad leis ar ais. Agus d'éirigh an *battle* ar ais ansin—agus d'imigh seisean.[5] Agus mharbh sí—mharbh sí Loinseachán.

Agus nuair a bhí sí ag dul soir Mín an Ghriobaigh, tháinig sí fhad leis ar ais. Agus scaoil sé Griobaigh léithi ansin agus thúsaigh sí féin agus Griobaigh a throid ansin.

Agus nuair a bhí sé ag dul amach Loch Muc, bhí sí aige ar ais.
Bhí Griobaigh marbh fosta aici. Agus b'éigean dó féin toisiú uirthi
ansin. Chuir sé — bhí sí ag cur crua leis, agus fuair sé a mhéar a chur
ina bhéal. Agus bhí an-fhead ghlaice[6] aige agus rinne sé fead glaice.

Dúirt an deirfiúr, Finngheal — bhí sí taobh thall den loch — dúirt
sí gur siúd fead an Fhearghamhain, cá bith áit a raibh sé.
Fearghamhain a bhéaradh siad air. Agus d'imigh sí. Bhí fhios aici
go raibh rud ínteacht ag teacht air. D'imigh sí agus tháinig sí anuas
fhad leis an loch.

Agus chuir sí trí clocha móra ina naprún agus tháinig sí trasna
an locha. Agus nuair a bhí sí trasna an locha, chóir a bheith,
mhoithigh sí fead eile. Shíl sí gurb é an taobh eile a bhí sé ansin agus
thiontóigh sí anonn ar ais an loch agus nuair a bhí sí taobh thall,
mhoithigh sí fead eile. D'aithin sí ansin gur taobh abhus[7] a bhí sé
agus thiontóigh sí ar ais. Agus bhí na trí clocha móra seo léithi ina
naprún. Agus nuair a bhí sí chóir a bheith ag teacht isteach an taobh
abhus, bhí gruag a cinn — bhí sí ag cíoradh a cinn nuair a mhoithigh
sí an chéad fhead — bhí gruag a cinn síos léithi. Chuaigh a cuid cosa
i bhfostó i ngruag a cinn agus báitheadh sa loch í.

Agus mharbh an mhuc an Fearghamhain agus mharbh seisean
an mhuc. Sin an fad atá sa scéal sin.

22

THE CALF-MAN

Well, the Calf-man lived back in Glencolmcille and he decided —
there was a sister of his living out there near Fintown — he decided
that he would come to visit her this day.

As he was leaving — there was a pig back that way in a place they
call The Pig's Hill in the Glen, and there was no-one that approached
the place where she had her lair that she didn't kill — but, as he was
leaving they forbade him to go near the pig.

"It is well you knew," says he, "that when you prohibited me from
doing that, that it was the very thing I must do."

The Calf-man headed off with his stick and he came up the Glen.
And when he got to the lair that the pig had — she had two piglets — he
flailed with his stick in it. He killed the two piglets. He left his stick
in the lair and walked on.

He had three dogs with him, a dog called *Loinseachán,* another called *Grathaigh* and a third called *Griobaigh.* Off he went and when he had gone a little bit, the pig came and found the dead piglets and the man gone.

The pig got the man's scent and she followed him and when he was going up by Mully, she caught up with him and he loosed *Bullaigh* at her. He made off as fast as he could then and the pig killed *Bullaigh* and set off after him once again.

So, when he was going out by Stralinchy, he loosed *Loinseachán* at her—she caught up with him again. And the battle started then— he made off. And she killed *Loinseachán.*

When he was going over by Meenagrubby, she caught up with him again. So, he loosed *Griobaigh* at her then and the fight between *Griobaigh* and her began.

So, by the time he was going out by Lough Muck, she had caught up with him again. She had killed *Griobaigh* too. So, he had to join battle with her then. He got—she was making things difficult enough for him and he managed to get his finger in his mouth. He had a powerful whistle and he whistled. Finngheal, his sister—she was on the other side of the lough—she said that that was [Goll's] whistle— The Calf-man's whistle, wherever he might be. He was called The Calf-man. So, away she went. She knew that he was in some difficulty or other. Off she went and she came down as far as the lough.

When—she put three big stones in her apron and she crossed over the lough and when she was nearly over, she heard another whistle. She thought it was on the other side and she turned back across the lough and when she was back over again, she heard another whistle. She realised then that it was on the other side and she turned back. She had these three big stones in her apron and when she had almost landed at the other side, her hair—she was combing her hair when she heard the first whistle—her hair was hanging loose and her feet got entangled in her hair and she was drowned in the lough.

So, the pig killed the Calf-man and he killed the pig. That's as far as that story goes.

This recording was made on 19.7.1972. Duration 3' 38". Tape 25/1 SÓC (9 cms.p.s.).

1

"Mo Dhoireagán, Mo Dhoireagán!"

Caesar Otway in his *Sketches in Ireland* (Dublin 1827) in describing his visit to Donegal noted that "the country on every side presents memorials of Columkill, the peculiar Saint of Tyrconnell" (52), later adding that our saint's fame followed him wherever he travelled through Donegal (136). In his *Heavy Hangs the Golden Grain* (Dublin 1951), Donegal writer, Séumas Mac Manus could observe that "the fields are full of legends of holy, witty, passionate Colm" (87). Closer again to our own time and drawing on his extensive experience as a full-time folklore collector in the field, Seán Ó hEochaidh presented a substantial review of Donegal legends of St Colm Cille in *Irisleabhar Muighe Nuadhat* (1963), p. 33-50, under the heading "Colm Cille sa tSeanchas" (*IMN*).

Something of the flavour of these stories of Donegal's own saint that so haunted and beguiled Otway and MacManus, stories that have lived on the lips of ordinary people for centuries, may be gained from the first eight items in this collection as told here by Pádraig Eoghain Phádraig Mac an Luain. In the McLoone household, Colm Cille was a popular subject of conversation and on the many occasions his name came up, not one, but a whole series of stories about him were told. In this collection, numbers 4, 2, 7, 8, 5 and 6, with another version of No. 3 completing the series, were told in that order on 29.12.1972 (Tape 24/1 SÓC). Numbers 4 and 1 here, together with number 8, were told in that sequence on 26.12.1973 (Tape 85/1 SÓC), while on 31.1.1975 (Tape 26/1 SÓC) the sequence was 4, 3, 1, 8 and 6. So as to allow them to assume a chronological order in broad agreement with the progress of the saint's career, these items, introduced by the quatrain on Derry, have had yet another sequence imposed upon them here.

To our storyteller, as to Séumas MacManus, the saint was simply "Colm" (Cf. Nos. 2, 4, 5 and 6) and Pádraig's view of him would not have differed much from that of Otway who called him — "a passionate pigeon of the Church, and very like a real Irishman — he was sometimes the best-humoured and softest-hearted fellow in the world; but vex him, and he would kick up such a row, set all about him fighting . . . breaking heads like a Tipperary faction on a fair green. . ."(*op. cit.*, 52).

The sort of stories about Colm Cille that Pádraig Eoghain Phádraig tells here were also current in Otway's day, of course, and, indeed, long before it, as can be judged from the numerous parallels that can be traced between folk legends of the saint and the accounts given of him in the 16th century *Betha Colaim Cille* (*BCC*) by Maghnus Úa Domhnaill or in the seventh-century *Vita Sancti Colombae* (*VSC*) by Adamnán, as also in *The Old Irish Life of Colum-cille* (*OIL*) — probably from the eleventh century.

72

For lists of books and articles referring to Colm Cille, cf. James F. Kenney, *The Sources for the Early History of Ireland: Ecclesiastical* (New York 1929), p. 422-3; "Bibliography of Donegal" by J. C. T. MacDonagh and Edward Mac Intyre in the *Donegal Annual (DA)*, Vol. 1, Part 1, p. 55; Anraí Mac Giolla Chomhaill, *Beatha Cholm Cille* (Baile Átha Cliath 1981), p. 29-30. "Manus O'Donnell and Irish Folk Tradition" (*Éigse* Vol. 8, Part 2 [1956-7], p. 108-32). In the latter, the author, Joseph Szövérffy, describes Manus O'Donnell as being "a Janus-head . . . looking back and forward, connecting in various ways modern Irish popular lore and medieval traditions" (127). This article is an important pioneering survey on the basis of which Szövérffy concludes that Manus O'Donnell made a considerable contribution "to the growth of Irish popular traditions" (132). This theme is also pursued in Szövérffy's "Manus O'Donnell-Studien" in *Irisches Erzählgut im Abendland* (Berlin 1957), p. 97-136.

Items No. 2-8, together with this opening quatrain in this *mélange* of Colm Cille lore, do not make up the entire corpus of folk tradition surrounding the saint, but rather provide a representative sample of it.

Colm Cille's leave-taking of Ireland and of Derry for exile in Scotland has been the subject and inspiration of numerous verses, many of them of considerable antiquity. The quatrain quoted here combines this theme with that of prophecy for which the saint was famous. In *BCC* § 90, p. 313, [*ZCP* 4]), the arrival in Derry of an English bishop ("*espoc gallda*") who would destroy the church built by Colm Cille, is forecast. In *NOK*, the following lines, which echo at least in part the sentiments of Pádraig Eoghain Phádraig's quatrain, occur:

> Scaelfedh m'oileach uair glan glé,
> Acus airgfidh mo Dhoire;
> Mo Dhoire! mo Dhoirigan!
> M'árus, agus m'aireaglan!
>
> Is mairg, a Dhé tola tar,
> Do (bh)-fuil ind dán a milladh!
> Ní biaidh   —   —   —

From the folk tradition of Co. Tyrone, Éamonn Ó Tuathail in *SML* 152 (cf. also Notes, 194) quotes the following version—

> A Dhoireagain, A Dhoireagain,
> Mo chrú-choill agus m'áilleagan,
> Mo chrádh go bhfuil se i ndán
> Do na Gallaibh bheith 'na gconuí
> Astuigh i lár mo Dhoireagain.

While Ó Tuathail's "*Mo chrú-choill*" may be translated as "My hazel nut", "*Mo chnó úll*", which Pádraig Eoghain Phádraig appears to say, is more difficult of interpretation. Two further versions taken down near the Croaghs, in Glenfinn, by Liam Mac Meanman and contained in IFC 185:421 and IFC 311:163 each have "*Mo chró mhaol*".

2

Pádraig agus Colm Cille

"*Pádraig a bheannaigh Éire uilig ach Gleann*", as Seán Ó hEochaidh says in *IMN*, 41. Various other parts of Ireland were also said to have escaped St. Patrick's blessing; in Donegal it is Glencolmcille which is accorded this role and which is also frequently referred to as being the headquarters of Fionn Mac Cumhaill and his Fianna (Cf. No. 21 in this collection). In *BCC*, Colm Cille's coming is prophesied not only by Saints Patrick and Brigid and a whole host of other Irish saints, but "also druids and persons who had not the faith foretold a long time before his birth that he would come. In proof whereof Finn Mac Cumhaill prophesied that he would come . . ." (*BCC* § 42, p. 545 [*ZCP* 3]).

3

Colm Cille agus "an Bíobla"

The story of the "bible" secretly copied by Colm Cille, which spawned the maxim "to every cow its calf and to every book its copy", first noticed in *BCC* § 168, p. 259-63 (*ZCP* 9), where the phrase used is "*le gach boin a boinin .i. a laogh agus le gach lebhur a leabhrán*", is widely quoted in a variety of 19th and 20th century sources, including, from Donegal, Maghtochair, "*Inishowen its history, traditions and antiquities*" (Derry 1807), p. 29-30; William Harkin, *Scenery and Antiquities of North West Donegal* (Londonderry 1893), p. 92-3; Stephen Gwynn, *Highways and Byways in Donegal and Antrim* (London 1899), p. 96; E. Maguire, *A History of the Diocese of Raphoe*, Part I (Dublin 1920), p. 419; J. J. Campbell, *Legends of Ireland*, (London 1955), p. 109-17. However, Seán Ó hEochaidh's *IMN* article makes no mention of this story, nor is it listed by the same authority in his compilation of Donegal legends about Colm Cille in IFC 2115. A Galway version of it in the Irish language appears in print in *Béaloideas* 21 (1951-2) No. 88, English summary 328-9 (= *Scéalta Cráibhtheacha* [cf. *LI*, 106]) and in IFC 694:179-82, we have one Donegal (Rosguill) version of it in the Irish language. There may well be others, but, in spite of its repeated appearances in print, this story does not appear to have gained any great popularity or to have achieved, among Irish-speakers, at least, the wide currency of other stories about the saint. I have not come across other versions from the Croaghs besides the one told here by Pádraig Eoghain Phádraig and another version of it by the same storyteller which can be found on Tape 26/1 SÓC (31.1.1975).

4

Colm Cille agus Ár Slánaitheoir

BCC § 78, p. 294-5 (*ZCP* 4) describes an incident involving Colm Cille and Our Lord in the guise of a poor man seeking alms, as in Pádraig Eoghain Phádraig's story, refused him, in this instance, by Colm Cille's servant. The motif of the miraculous growth of oats from dough cast in the fire (cp. D2157.2) and the explanation for the origin of mice and rats are missing in the *BCC* version. *BCC* § 78 also notes, however, that "it was shewn unto (Colm Cille) to know the mind and intent of sea-reptiles and to understand the singing of the birds of the air" and elsewhere Colm Cille's power over dumb creatures (especially fish) is emphasized (cf. § 83, p. 303 and § 97, p. 321 [*ZCP* 4]). In *VSC*, 102-3 and in *BCC* § 79, the story of a miraculous harvest of barley, sown and reaped at the end of the summer season, is told.

In *IMN*, 38-9, and in his Colm Cille Ms. (IFC 2115: 79-80, 104-6), Seán Ó hEochaidh gives versions of this story as it is told here, minus the origin of rats and mice motif; other such Donegal versions can be found in *CC*, 91-2 (= *Gaelic Journal* 11 [1900], p. 149) and in *Béaloideas* 21 (1951-2), No. 12, Notes 284, English summary 305 (= *Scéalta Cráibhtheacha*). In the latter connection, Seán Ó Súilleabháin also observes that this story was frequently told with reference to St Martin. *LSIC* 1 (Notes 415 and English summary 465-6) contains a story linking the origin of rats, mice, pigs and cats with St Martin. A re-telling in English of this story as I got it from Pádraig Eoghain Phádraig can be found in *ILL*, 57.

At least seventeen IFC Ms versions of this story are known to me from all over Co. Donegal, none of them, however, from the Croaghs. Tape 24/1 SÓC (29.12.1972) and Tape 26/1 SÓC (31.1.1975) contain two other versions of this story taken down from Pádraig Eoghain Phádraig Mac an Luain.

5

Colm Cille agus na Bradáin a Leag é

Frequent reference is made in *BCC* to Colm Cille's power over fish (Cf. Notes to No. 4); he also *blesses* rivers (§ 75. p. 289 [*ZCP* 4]; §§ 133, 134, p. 57 and § 141, p. 69 [*ZCP* 5]: § 302, p. 325-7 [*OKS*]) and in *VSC*, 124-5 we are told that on one occasion fish was specially provided by God for the saint. *BCC* § 115, p. 31 (*ZCP* 5) tells how Colm Cille cursed the fishermen of Mulroy Bay, ordaining that they "would never have two fires in the same village" and that the bay would never have fish "caught in it from that out".

Pádraig Eoghain Phádraig's story of Colm Cille's curse, leading to the banishment of salmon from Lough Finn, centres round another well-known motif — that of the wrath of a saint or holy man reading by a riverside when water is splashed on his book by a trout or, alternatively, crossing a river and being tumbled into the water by leaping salmon, holy wrath that leads to a curse being placed on those waters rendering them devoid of fish forever.

Two other versions of this story are known to me from the Croaghs, one (IFC 992:234-5) taken down from Peadar Mac Giolla Dhiarmada in May 1947 (cf. Áine Ní Dhíoraí, *Scéalta agus Seanchas as na Cruacha i dTír Chonaill*, unpublished M.A. thesis, Department of Modern Irish, University College Dublin = *SSC*), the other taken down from Seán Mac an Bháird and published in *Béaloideas* 33 (1965), p. 117, the collector on both occasions being Seán Ó hEochaidh. Both these informants identify the "stepping stones" as being at "*Cor(a) Ghoill*" (cf. my *PIK*, 100).

H

6

Tairngreacht Cholm Cille

The retailing of the prophecies of Colm Cille and other local prophets ("Mac Amhlaoibh" in Cork, cf. *SAIL*, 206-10, Notes 430; "Brian Rua Ó Cearbháin" in Mayo, cf. Micheál Ó Tiománaidhe, *Targaireacht Bhriain Ruaidh Uí Chearbháin* (Dublin 1906) and "Domhnall an Chinn" in Donegal, cf. *SS*, No. 119, p. 282-5, Notes p. 380; *CC*, 77-80 and Liam Mac Meanman, "Folklore from Glenfinn", *DA*, Vol. 5, No. 1 [1981], p. 117-9.) was a common practice and one which often gave rise to confusion of the prophets and their various prophecies. Pádraig Eoghain Phádraig, for example, generally spoke of Colm Cille and the Glenfinn prophet, Domhnall an Chinn, in the same breath (cf. Tape 26/1 [31.1.1975]), as does his brother, Conall, here. Later during this recording session Pádraig declared that the prophecy recited by Conall had really been made by "Caitlín Nic Eachráin" for an account of whom, cf. *CC*, 77-80. *BCC* contains numerous references to Colm Cille's gift of prophecy and his exercise of it. *NOK*, constituting a collection of the "prophetic fragments" attributed to Colm Cille and other saints — but known to be largely the author's own invention — was published in 1850 (republished 1932). For other selections of Colm Cille's prophecies, cf. Leslie W. Lucas, *More about Mevagh* (Ballyshannon 1965), p. 1-2 (drawn from IFC Ms. sources), Séumas Mac Manus, *The Rocky Road to Dublin* (Dublin 1947), p. 128-9 and *LI*, 106.

7

Bás Cholm Cille

In *VSC*, 226-7, we are told that as the hour of Colm Cille's death drew near the faithful white horse "which used to carry the milk pails to and fro between the byre and the monastery" ran up to the saint and, as this account says, "wonderful to tell, lays his head against his breast — inspired, as I believe, by God . . . knowing that his master was soon about to leave him, and that he would see him no more, began to whinny, and to shed copious tears into the lap of the Saint as though he had been a man, and weeping and foaming at the mouth". *OIL*, 503 provides us with a similar account and mention of this incident is also made in *BCC* § 361, p. 409-50 (*OKS*); the introduction to *OKS* (xvii-xviii) also treats of this.

Neither *VSC* or *OIL* offer any details about Colm Cille's burial and it is left to *BCC* §§ 370, 371, p. 421-3 (*OKS*) to contrive an explanation for the transfer of Colm's body from Iona to Ireland: ". . . they put him in a coffin and buried him worshipfully in Iona. . . And Mandar son of the King of Lochlan came with a fleet of war to the monastery and plundered it and its graves, and tore up its tombs and lifted its coffins to search for booty therein. And they bare away with them the coffin of wood wherein was the body of Columcille. And they deemed it a coffer wherein was gold or silver or other treasure of the world, and they bare it away to their vessel on the sea and opened it not. And when they had put to sea, they opened the coffer. And when they found naught therein save the body of a man, they shut it again on the body and cast it in the sea. And it came to pass . . . that the coffin made never a stay until it came to Dún da Lethglas [Downpatrick]."

8

Cónair Cholm Cille

This story of the discovery of Colm Cille's coffin on its miraculous return to Ireland has been noted by Seán Ó hEochaidh in his Colm Cille Ms (IFC 2115: 46, 67), in a version taken down from Anna Nic an Luain of the Croaghs. The same collector also recorded a second Croaghs version from Cáit Bean Mhic Ghiolla Dhiarmada in June 1947. (IFC 992: 425-6 [cf. *SSC*, 203]). Two Galway versions, both in the Irish language, appear in *Béaloideas* 2 (1930), p. 384-5 and *Béaloideas* 21 (1951-2), No. 88, p. 199-202 (= *Scéalta Cráibhtheacha* [*LI*, 106-8]). P. Kennedy, *Legends of Mt. Leinster* (Dublin 1855), p. 281 ff. contains a version in English as does *BBIF*, 77-8 (from Pádraig Eoghain Phádraig [trans.]).

VSC, 156-7 provides an echo of this story in describing an incident involving the miraculous retrieval of what it calls "the milk-skin which the ebb-tide carried away and the flood-tide deposited again in its former place".

Tape 85/1 SÓC (26.12.1973) and Tape 26/1 SÓC (3.1.1975) contain two further versions of this story told by Pádraig Eoghain Phádraig in both of which Downpatrick and not, as here, Inishowen, are given as Colm Cille's place of burial.

9

Cailleach Ghallda ina Gearria

This story (ML 3055, *The Witch that was Hurt*) and Nos. 10 and 11 following, detail means and methods of stealing milk or the "profit" from it by magic means. In Ireland, the existence of the tradition concerning the metamorphosis of hag to hare was first noted by a twelfth-century visitor, Giraldus Cambrensis (cf. J. J. O'Meara, 'Giraldus Cambrensis in Topographia Hibernico, Text of the First Recension' [*Proceedings of the Royal Irish Academy*, 52, Section C, No. 4, p. 113]). It is a phenomenon which is also a matter of frequent comment in much later sources and, indeed, a widespread belief which may still be encountered in many parts of the country. For further notes and information on this subject, cf. *LSIC*, p. 437; *Béaloideas* 6 (1936), p. 261-2; *Béaloideas* 7 (1937), p. 78-81 and George Ewart Evans, *The Leaping Hare* (London 1972), particularly Chapter 13 "The Hare as Witch", p. 127-77 and p. 145, 215. For a comprehensive review of Nordic traditions about milk-stealing creatures (incorporating some British and Irish material), cf. Jan Wall, *Tjuvmjölkande väsen* (2 Vols. [Nos. 3 and 5] in the series *Studia Ethnologica Upsaliensia* [Uppsala 1977, 1978]). Another translation of this story, as taken down from Pádraig Eoghain Phádraig, appears in *ILL*, 25-6.

In the Croaghs, two versions of this story were recorded by Liam Mac Meanman, one from Jimmy Gubain on 27.2.1936 (IFC 185: 9-10), the other from Anna Nic an Luain on 9.5.1936 (IFC 171: 502). In or around that time, Mac Meanman also recorded five other versions of this story from various informants in the surrounding district. One of these (IFC 187: 14-5) also designates the hag/hare as a member of the local minority Protestant community, calling her "*cailleach phiseogach Alabnaigh i Mín na Gualanna*" — "a superstitious Scottish (i.e. Protestant) hag from Meenagolan".

In this recording, the voice in the background chiming in with such comments as "*Dia ár sábháil*" ("God save us") and agreeing with the storyteller that the whole business was, in truth, "*obair an diabhail*" ("the devil's work") is that of Pádraig Eoghain Phádraig's sister, Máire. Pádraig's own final comment "*Sin pisreogaí agat!*" ("There's superstition for you!") echoes my original enquiry for information on the general topic of "*pisreogaí*", its tone, perhaps, hinting at a degree of detachment, even scepticism, on the part of the storyteller.

10

"*Come all to me! Come all to me!*"

In the Glenfinn/Fintown area in 1936, eight versions of this story were recorded by Liam Mac Meanman. To the best of my knowledge, the story was not recorded by him or anyone else in the Croaghs, though, undoubtedly, it was also well-known there. A Donegal version from the parish of Glencolmcille appears in *SS*, 84-5 and other printed versions can be found in *Béaloideas* 1 (1927), p. 325; *Béaloideas* 7 (1937), p. 78-9 and *Béaloideas* 9 (1939), p. 32-3. Another translation of this story as taken down from Pádraig Eoghain Phádraig occurs in *ILL*, 26-7.

11

An Maistreadh Mór

This story, in common with Nos. 9 and 10 in this collection, forms part of the large body of lore surrounding milk and attempts to steal it, or the good of it, by supernatural means. The "*maistreadh mór*" referred to here was also sometimes carried out by hammering nails into the churn, while the placing of an ember beneath the churn was a common method of guarding against the depredations of ill-intentioned neighbours bent on stealing the "profit" of the milk.

The strong local identification given this story by Pádraig Eoghain Phádraig is also a feature of the only other Croaghs version of it known to me, a version called "*Maistriú Mór Chruach an Airgid*", collected by Seán Ó hEochaidh on 2.7.1948 from Seán Mac an Bháird (IFC 1101: 336-7 [cf. *SSC*, 179]). A re-telling in English of this story, as taken down from Pádraig Eoghain Phádraig, appears in *ILL*, 27.

12

Fidiléir an aon Phoirt amháin agus Gasúr de chuid na Sí

This story seems to have been known in one form or other in many parts of Ireland — cf. John Harrison "The man who learnt his music from the fairies" (unpublished 2nd Year Term Essay in the Department of Irish Folklore, University College Dublin). A Donegal version from the lips of Micí Simey Doherty (cf. p. 00), who gives the fiddler's name as Herron (a fairly common Glenfinn surname), may well have been the source for the version published here and for another version which I recorded from Pádraig Eoghain Phádraig's brother, Conall (Tape 68/1 SÓC [17.11.1973]). IFC Disc No. 853 (recorded in 1949) and BBC Disc Nos. 21348 and 21347 (recorded in 1951) contain two recordings in English of Mící Simey Doherty's telling of this story, as well as a rendition of the tune said to have been learnt from the fairies.

13

An Sagart agus na Síógaí

ML 5050, *The Fairies' Prospect of Salvation,* the international legend type to which this story belongs, has been treated in its Irish context by Micheál Briody under the heading "Súil na síóg le Slánú" (unpublished 3rd Year Term Essay in the Department of Irish Folklore at University College Dublin). One of the fifty-six versions listed there is a version collected from Pádraig Eoghain Phádraig Mac an Luain by Seán Ó hEochaidh under the title *"Bráthair Dhún na nGall agus an slua aerach"* (IFC 1412: 184). This same version appears in print in *Béaloideas* 23 (1954), p. 142-3 and was reprinted with accompanying English translation in *SS,* 260-1 (Notes 373, 386). One other story— "Slua Sí an Aeir a Ghoid an tArbhar"—collected by Seán Ó hEochaidh from our storyteller—has a similar history, being first published in *Béaloideas* 27 (1959), p. 24-5 and subsequently reprinted with English translation in *SS,* 268-71 (Notes 386).

In May 1947. Cáit Bean Mhic Giolla Dhiarmada supplied Seán Ó hEochaidh with the only other Croaghs version of this story known to me (IFC 992: 276-7 [cf. *SSC,* 173]), apart from that which Máire Uí Cheallaigh, herself a native of the Croaghs (cf. p. 84, 85), recently contributed to *An tUltach,* (Vol. 60, No. 9, p. 18-9). Liam Mac Meanman (IFC 169: 514-5, 186: 412-4) and Seán Ó hEochaidh (IFC 1641: 59-80) have collected three further versions from areas bordering the Croaghs while, in *Béaloideas* 1, No. 2 (1927), p. 158, Éamonn Ó Tuathail published a Donegal version from Cloghaneely and in *Ulster Folklore* (London 1913), p. 54-5, Elizabeth Andrews prints an English-language version from Inishowen in the same county.

14

Conall agus na Daoine Beaga

Pádraig Eoghain Phádraig's account of his brother's encounter with the fairy folk, recited in the latter's hearing, is told with great conviction. The description he gives of the appearance of the fairies is typical of such accounts, as is the notice drawn to the inability of human kind to understand fairy speech. English-speakers often ascribe the difficulty in interpreting fairy speech to the fact that they were speaking Irish.

15

An Fear a Phós an Mhaighdean Mhara

ML 4080, *The Seal Woman*, the story of the man who married the mermaid (many references to which can be found in the material classified in *TIF* under *AT* 1889H Submarine Otherworld), is one of the best known stories of the Irish coast and hundreds of versions of it appear in manuscript and printed sources. Its continuing popularity is borne out by the frequency with which it has been noted in recent years in various parts of the country. The version printed here is one of a number of tellings of it by Pádraig Eoghain Phádraig. Tape 84/i SÓC (28.12.1974) contains another and a third version of it was recorded from him in 1977 for the RTÉ film *"Béaloideas:* The People's Past".

The occurrence, and, indeed, the popularity of this story (two other versions of it have been collected in the Croaghs), in a landlocked mountainous area of Donegal such as the Croaghs may be explained by the lively contact which people from the Croaghs and other mountain dwellers maintained with coastal Donegal at places like Narin and Portnoo, both of which lie in the vicinity of Cashelgoland where the action takes place and where the descendants of the mermaid are said to have lived. The surprising amount of sea and seashore vocabulary contained in *DD* and *SCC* may also be accounted for by connections such as these.

Pádraig Eoghain Phádraig's old friend, Peadar Ó Tiománaí—by Pádraig's own admission the source of many of his pieces—was Seán Ó hEochaidh's informant in June 1947 for one of the remaining Croaghs versions of this story (IFC 992: 368-71 [cf. *SSC*, 170-2]). The same informant contributed another version, recorded by Caoimhín Ó Danachair in 1948 (IFC Disc No. M439) and transcribed many years later by Seán Ó hEochaidh (IFC 1947: 101-2). On that occasion, yet another version was recorded on disc from Anna Nic an Luain, (IFC Disc No. M435A) and this too was subsequently transcribed by Seán Ó hEochaidh (IFC 1947: 7-8). On another disc recording, (IFC Disc No. M384-5), Anna Nic an Luain renders five verses of the song said to have been composed by the husband forsaken by the mermaid (transcribed by Seán Ó hEochaidh in IFC 1946: 298-9). while in IFC 992: 488, Seán Ó hEochaidh contributes two verses of this song from the same informant. All three Croaghs informants, Pádraig Eoghain Phádraig Mac an Luain, Peadar Ó Tiománaí and Anna Nic an Luain clearly identify the forsaken husband as a man called Gallagher from Cashelgoland, a detail which is confirmed in a handful of versions of this same story recorded by Liam Mac Meanman in various other parts of the parish of Inniskeel (cf. IFC 187: 45-6; IFC 260: 199-200, 294-5, 414-5 and IFC 366: 229-30). None of these latter versions include the husband's song or make any mention of it. Pádraig Eoghain Phádraig in this recording, "sings" the only two verses of this song known to him (cf. p. xxiv). Elsewhere, versions of a song associated with the "Man Marries Mermaid" story have been recorded from Cití Ní Ghallchobhair of Gweedore, Co. Donegal, by the former Irish Folklore Commission, the BBC and by Radio Éireann.

The version of this story and the song associated with it, taken down from Pádraig Eoghain Phádraig's father can be found in *CC*, 83-4. For a discussion of this legend type, cf. Otto Anderson, "Seal-Folk in East and West. Some comments on a fascinating group of folk tales" in *Folklore International* (Essays in traditional literature, belief and custom in honor of Wayland Debs Hand [Hatboro 1967]), p. 1-6; William A. Lessa, *Tales from Ulithi Atoll, A Comparative Study in Oceanic Folklore,* Folklore Studies 13, University of California Press, Berkeley and Los Angeles, 1961 (esp. Chapter 15 "Tale Type: The Porpoise Girl" [The Swan Maiden] p. 120-67; David Thomson, *The People of the Sea* (London 1965).

16

An Siosánach

The *story of An Siosánach* (generally surnamed Ó Baoill, though also called Ó Cuinn (IFC 171: 909-10), Ó Scannlain (IFC 1170: 39-42 [cf. *SSC,* 184-5]) and Ó Dónaill (IFC 185: 261, IFC 186: 301-2) and the story of *An Fearghamhain* (No. 22, p. 69) probably are the two most popular stories told in the Croaghs and surrounding area. Placenames and the desire to explain them may lie at the heart of that popularity — the *"Bealach na gCreach"* of this story providing ample scope for speculation in that regard.

A strong local tradition of travellers and "car-men" on their way from Glenties to Strabane being subjected to robbery and violence, giving *Bealach na gCreach* much the same reputation as Barnesmore on the southern slopes of the Blue Stack Mountains (cf. *DA* Vol. 3 [1956], p. 114-6 and Vol. 5, No. 1 [1961], p. 59, 62), provides the basis for one commonly offered explanation of the name.

More persistent, however, is the tradition of cattle raiding from Connacht, embodied in the story of *An Siosánach.* One version of this story lays the blame for such activities on neighbours to the east rather than the south — *"Thigeadh bunadh Chontae Dhoire aníos go Dún na nGall. . ."* ("the people of Co. Derry used to come up to Donegal. . ." [IFC 185: 14-7]). The name for such raids — *"Creacha Baiollach"* (*Baiollach* or "Boylagh" being a Barony name) is given by our storyteller here and the memory of their perpretators is perpetuated in the local saying *"An Connachtach bradach"* ("The thieving Connachtman"). For further information on Donegal "Creaghts", cf. Dennis Verschoyle "Background to a Hidden Age", *DA* Vol. 6 (1965), p. 110-25.

For versions of the "Siosánach" story in print, cf. *SCC,* 9, *OA,* 34-6 (notes p. 73) and *CC,* 81-2. The *"Lá Thadhg na dTadhgann"* in the title and text of Laoide's versions is repeated here and in other manuscript versions. It is also called *"Lá Seon Dick . . . lá nach dtáinig agus nach dtig"* (IFC 187: 58).

Three of the four manuscript versions from the Croaghs were recorded by Liam Mac Meanman — from Jimmy Gubain on 27.2.1936 (IFC 185: 14-7), Johnny Mac Aoidh on 5.2.1936 (IFC 171: 579) and Amras Mac Dhuibhfhinn on 8.7.1936 (IFC 171: 909-10). About the same time, he also recorded four other versions in the surrounding district (IFC 171: 91-2, IFC 185: 261, IFC 186: 301-2 and IFC 187: 56-8). The fourth Croaghs version was recorded on 22.4.1949 from Pádraig Ó Giobúin by Seán Ó hEochaidh (IFC 1170: 39-47).

17

Clainn tSuibhne na Miodóg

Feall Chloinn tSuibhne "The Treachery of the Sweeneys" is the name given to
the only other version of this story I know of, illustrating both how the Sweeneys
acquired this reputation and how they earned the "Dagger" soubriquet. That
particular version was recorded on 6.5.1937 from Anna Nic Cailín (60) of Kingarrow
on the northern fringe of Inniskeel Parish by Liam Mac Meanman (IFC 348: 122-3).
Henry Morris in *Béaloideas* 9 (1939), p. 291 makes mention of the "Dagger" but
not the "Treachery"—

       The Mac Sweeneys, who do not belong to the Cinel Conaill, were brought
    into Tír Conaill from Scotland as gallowglasses. When O'Donnell lived in
    state at Donegal or Ballyshannon the three most remote parts of his territory
    were Banagh, Doagh, and Fanad. So O'Donnell brought over three branches
    of the Mac Sweeneys and settled them down in these three districts. The Four
    Masters frequently style them "O'Donnells constables". Their duty was not
    alone "to rise out" in case of war, but to see that the inhabitants of these
    more or less inaccessible districts paid their tribute and helped O'Donnell
    in his wars. Their great weapon was the *tuagh* or battle-axe. But when the
    English established the British peace over Tír Chonaill, this battle-axe was
    banned. But the spirit of fight was so strong in the *Clann tSuibhne* that they
    could not be reconciled to be entirely disarmed, so they carried a knife
    called in Gaelic both in Ireland and Scotland a *meadóg*, whence they have
    often been termed Clann tSuibhne na Meadóg. Carried in the leather belt,
    it was inconspicuous under a *cóta mór*. But it was dangerously conspicuous
    when the blood of a Mac Sweeney grew hot under a real or supposed injury
    or insult.
       A humane land agent in the Banagh-Boylagh district was so convinced
    of this that he resolved to get the Mac Sweeneys broken off this habit of
    carrying the *meadóg*, so he published that he would accept a *meadóg* in lieu
    of a half year's rent from each of the Mac Sweeneys, provided the latter
    solemnly promised never to wear one again. The generous offer succeeded.
    Each Mac Sweeney came in and threw his *meadóg* on the floor. These were
    carefully gathered up and securely stowed away or buried, so that you might
    offer to-day a huge reward for a *meadóg* and not get one.
       The Mac Sweeneys are first mentioned in the Annals of the Four Masters
    at 1352, and between that and the Flight of the Earls, that is, in two and
    a half centuries, they are mentioned nearly three hundred times for their
    exploits.

Pádraig Mac Seáin, in the course of his essay "Seanchas fá Chlainn tSuibhne
agus fá Tharlach Mac Suibhne, an Píobaire Mór" (*Béaloideas* 32 [1964], p. 71-84)
while stating (of the Sweeneys)—"*Is iomdha fó-scéal, agus is iomdha scéal
creathnaitheach a chuala mé ina dtaoibh*" (p. 71) makes no reference to our story
other than to mention "*Cloinn tSuibhne na Miodóg*" initially and later (p. 75)
recount a different incident involving a *meadóg* thrown by a member of the Sweeney

family, as an illustration of their treacherous character. This incident is said to have caused the comment — "*nárbh é an fia fíor an té a dúirt an chéad lá ariamh go mbeidh feall i gCloinn tSuibhne a fhad is bhéas ball dubh ar an fheadóig!*"

"*Feall na h-aon oidhche*" is the name of an item recorded by Pádraig Mac an Ghoill of Ardara, Co. Donegal and published by him in *Béaloideas* 8 (1938), p. 110. It tells how the "Lochlannaigh" (Pádraig Eoghain Phádraig's "Danes") were all laid low in the course of one night in an act of extraordinary co-ordination by an Irish nation incensed at their continued invocation of *Ius primae noctis.*

18

An Fear Mór

This story, incorporating *AT 1544, The Man who Got a Night's Lodging* and *AT 1115, Attempted Murder with Hatchet,* is known to me in three other versions from the Croaghs, two of them taken down from Anna Nic an Luain. The first of these was taken down by Liam Mac Meanman on 6.2.1936 (IFC 171: 659-64) and it is called "*Scéal an Bhig Man*" as is her second version, taken down by Seán Ó hEochaidh on 30.10.1947 (IFC 1032: 346-353). "Big Man" rather than "*Fear Mór*" is preferred by the storyteller throughout these two tellings. The third Croaghs version, taken down by Liam Mac Meanman from Paidí Mac Aoidh on 14.4.1937 (IFC 335: 361-3), uses neither appellation but refers instead to a "*fear siúil*" ("a tramp") and only contains the *AT 1544* element of the story. A re-telling of this story, containing both the above mentioned tale types, appears in print in Seumas Mac Manus, *Donegal Fairy Stories* (London 1902) p. 77-93 under the title "Manis the Miller".

19

An Crochaire Tarnocht

This story is known to me in three other versions taken down in the Croaghs by full-time collectors Liam Mac Meanman and Seán Ó hEochaidh. Micheál Mac an Luain (cf. p. xxxiv) had this story recorded from him on 4.2.1936 by the former (IFC 171: 526-41) and Seán Mac an Bháird (cf. p. xxxiv) was Seán Ó hEochaidh's informant on 1.8.1947 (IFC 1032: 151-64) and again in December 1948 (IFC 1949: 44-60 [Disc No. M404]) when he contributed a fine version on a disc recording made by the former Irish Folklore Commission (cf. p. xxxi). These storytellers were well-known to Pádraig Eoghain Phádraig and it is probable that the version told by him here derives from their somewhat longer and fuller tellings.

All four Croaghs versions concentrate heavily on the central theme of what Bruford calls "the treacherous deceiver" thwarted by the hero (*Gaelic Folk-Tales and Medieval Romances* (= *Béaloideas* 34, [1966 (1969)]), p. 128 and Note 37, p. 132. Pádraig Eoghain Phádraig's version incorporates *AT 302, The Ogre (Devil's) Heart in the Egg,* as do the other three versions from the Croaghs.

The Donegal stories published under the titles "An Crochaire Tárnocht" (by Fergus Mac Róigh [Enrí Ó Muirgheasa] in *MS*, 20-33) and "Eamonn Ua Cíorrthais (?)" (by E. C. Quiggin in *DD*, p. 201-13) diverge significantly from Pádraig Eoghain Phádraig's version of "An Crochaire Tarnocht", incorporating various other tale types (such as *AT 300, The Dragon Slayer*) and, in the case of Ó Muirgheasa's story (which originated in Teelin, Co. Donegal), dispensing entirely with the notion of suspension of a substitute in the noose.

An Crochaire Tarnocht appears in a similar sanitized role in the Munster versions of the story called "Bladhman Mac an Ubhaill" (AT 300) — cf., for example, *Béaloideas* 1, Part 3 (1928) p. 226-237 and *Béaloideas* 5, p. 3-21 and for an English language version, "Blaiman, Son of Apple in the Kingdom of the White Strand" in Jeremiah Curtin, *Hero-Tales of Ireland* (London 1894), p. 373-408.

20

An Toirtín Beag agus an Toirtín Mór

This story — called "*Scéal* Jig Jag" by the storyteller — is a version of *AT 480, The Spinning-Women by the Spring. The Kind and Unkind Girls* — and is known to me in four other tellings from the Croaghs, three of them taken down by full-time collectors Liam Mac Meanman and Seán Ó hEochaidh. Liam Mac Meanman's informant on 6.2.1936 was a young man from Cró an Chaorthainn on the south face of the Blue Stack Mountain range (IFC 171: 693-703) while the versions recorded by Seán Ó hEochaidh were both told by Anna Nic an Luain, one on 30.2.1948 (IFC 1033: 213-9) and the other in December 1948 (IFC 1949: 286-97, Disc No. M427), on which latter occasion the recording was made on gramophone disc (cf. p. xxxi). The fourth Croaghs version (IFC S1049: 456-60) was taken down in 1937 from her father (Amras Mac Dhuibhfhinn) by Máire Ní Dhuibhfhinn (= Máire Uí Cheallaigh), then a child attending Croaghs National School.

A Donegal version of this story called "The Old Hag's Long Leather Bag" appears in Seumas Mac Manus *Donegal Fairy Stories* (London 1902), p. 235-56.

21

Goll Mac Morna

Three other versions of this story are known to me from the Croaghs. In June 1947, Aodh Mac an Luain supplied Seán Ó hEochaidh with a version entitled "*Carraic Ghoill*" (IFC 992: 377-9) and Peadar Ó Tiománaí (cf. p. xxvi) and Seán Mac an Bháird (cf. p. xxxiv), within days of each other in February 1936, provided Liam Mac Meanman with two more versions, respectively entitled "*Goll sa Cheó*" (IFC 171: 586-7) and "*Goll ag dóghadh na mban*" (IFC 171: 923-4). The person named by Pádraig Eoghain Phádraig as the source for his version is Róise Mhic an Luain — "*Croí na Féile*" (cf. *SCC*, 15-22) — the mother of Seán Ó hEochaidh's informant, Aodh Mac an Luain. Pádraig's telling of this story corresponds closely to the version told by Seán Mac an Bháird (IFC 171: 923-4) including the "loss of hair" episode more properly associated with Conán Maol.

In his telling of this story, Pádraig Eoghain Phádraig identifies *"Carraig Ghoill"* rather hazily as being *"síos fá na Rosa"* ("down in the Rosses"). One of Liam Mac Meanman's Rosguill (Co. Donegal) informants, in the course of listing local placenames, notes — *"Carra Ghoill (i.e. Carraig Ghoill) an áit ar fhan Goll Mac Moirne naoi lá agus fiche ag ól sáile gan bhia gan deoch ach ag ól sáile nuair a léim sé amach as Dumhaigh go dtí Carra Ghoill . . . cibé ar bith mar fuair sé isteach chan fhuil fhios agamsa"* (IFC 171: 538). *"Méarthóg Ghuill"*, described as being *"carraig mhór sa bhfairrge ar an taobh thuaidh de Chonndae Mhuigheó"* (*An Claidheamh Soluis* II, 2, Meitheamh 2, 1900, p. 188) ("a large rock in the sea to the north of County Mayo") is also associated with Goll, as its name "Goll's Pebble" proclaims.

Goll's Parting with his wife", "The Death of Goll" and "The War-Vaunt of Goll" are the names given to three Fenian lays with which this story has connections. The Irish texts (with English translations) have been edited by Eoin Mac Néill in *Duanaire Finn 1* (*Irish Texts Society* 7 [1904]), p. 23-4 (121.2), 58-61 (165-9) and 86-92 (200-8); extensive notes and commentaries to these lays are provided in *Duanaire Finn 3* (Irish Texts Society 43 [1953]), p. 22-3, 49-52 and 76-85, by Gearóid Ó Murchadha. Pádraig Eoghain Phádraig's story is in large part a prose rendering of "The Death of Goll" with only Goll's final words from the rock finding an echo in the actual lays themselves. Cf. also in this context An Seabhac, *Laoithe na Féine* (Dublin 1941), p. 257-9. *OA*, 51-3 contains another version of our story and *IT*, 109 contains a verse similar to the one recited here.

22

An Fearghamhain

This story was very popular in the parish of Inniskeel where Lough Finn and all the other places mentioned in it lie. It was also known in other parts of Donegal, but, apparently, not outside that county. It has made frequent appearance in Irish and in English in various books dealing with aspects of life and language in Donegal.

From the Croaghs, five versions are known to me — two of them taken down by full-time collector Seán Ó hEochaidh, the first of these from Aodh Mac an Luain in June 1947 (IFC 992: 379-84) and the second, a much abbreviated version, from Anna Nic an Luain on 14.7.1948 (IFC 1101: 423); full-time collector Liam Mac Meanman recorded one version from Johnny Mac Aoidh on 5.2.1936 (IFC 171: 583-5) and another from Amras Mac Dhuibhfhinn on 8.2.1936 (IFC 171: 911-4), the latter informant in 1937 also supplying a version to his daughter Máire (= Máire Uí Cheallaigh), then a school child attending Croaghs National School (IFC S1049: 261-5 [cf. *SSC*, 26-9]). Like the other Croaghs' versions of this story, Pádraig Eoghain Phádraig's version shows uncertainty with regard to the identity of the places named after *Fearghamhain's* hounds, but the story is still very far from being a "mere folk etymology of some townland names" as Seosamh Laoide described the version he collected for his *CC* (cf. notes, p. 117). For a note on the confusion of the names of dogs and places in this story, cf. *PIK*, 136.

A rather grandiose rendering of this story in verse by John O'Donovan can be found in his Ordnance Survey Letters from Donegal written in 1835 (Ts. 102-3, Ms. 183-6 [other references to the story can be found in Ts. 96, Ms. 174 and Ts. 115, Ms. 203]). O'Donovan's version in verse was reprinted in William James Doherty, *Inis-Owen and Tir Connell* (Dublin 1891), p. 78-83 and in William Harkin, *Scenery and Antiquities of North West Donegal* (Londonderry 1893), p. 81-3. English-language prose versions appeared in *Transactions of the Ossianic Society*, 5 (1860), p. 165 and in *The Donegal Highlands* (*op. cit.*), 160-2.

Apart from the version published by Laoide, other Irish versions were published by Fergus Mac Róigh (= Énrí Ó Muirgheasa) in *MS*, 34-7 (and notes p. 54-8), by Éamonn Ó Tuathail in *Béaloideas*, Vol. 1, No. 1 (1927), p. 54-7; by Alf Sommerfelt in *Lochlann* 3, p. 387-8 and by Art Hughes in *An tUltach*, Vol. 60, Nos. 6-7 (1983), p. 31-2.

DIALECT NOTES TO TEXTS 1-11, 13-22

1

" *Mo Dhoireagán, Mo Dhoireagán!* "

1. [ʃɛhən] for *seisean* occurs *passim* in Texts 12, 14, 15, 16, 18, 19, 20, 21 and 22. Cf. *GTh* § 491 [ɛsə heʃən / ɛsə heʃə]. Cf. Note 2, Text 22.
2. Examples of very strongly velarized unlenited *l*-sounds, which are a feature of this speaker's pronunciation, occur elsewhere in these texts. For a similar development in the Irish of Rathlin Island, cf. *IRI* § 40.

2

Pádraig agus Colm Cille

1. For a discussion of the sound [λ:] and its distribution in Ulster Irish, cf. *DD* §§ 81-8; *LASID* I, p. 177, 220, 223; *GTh* §§ 201, 549 (ii) and *CCUS* § 18.6. Three further examples of this sound occur in the following text (*oícheannaí, daoine, saol*) and numerous other examples can be found elsewhere in this collection.

3

Colm Cille agus " An Bíobla "

1. Cf. [m'i:blə and *banfán* > [manəwan] (*DT* § 388) and for other examples of the development of b>m, *IA* §§ 507, 1337, 1605c (*beachóg > meachóg*); *IE* § 465 (*beach > meach*); *CCUS* § 3.4 (*banríon > máiríon*). For the distribution of the various forms of the word for " bee ", cf. *LASID* 1, p. 49.
2. *Paróiste* is a feminine noun in Ulster Irish, as is *contae* (Text 2).
3. *Dhíth* is generally pronounced with a short vowel in this dialect (cf. Text 14 [ə jɛh]). Cf. *LASID* 1, p. 24; *LASID* 4, p. 134 (No. 74a), p. 136 (No. 296) and p. 141 (No. 1045)—Point 83. I have also heard [ə jɔh] (cf. *LASID* 4, p. 144 [Point 83]). Cf. also Text 12—*i rith* [ə rüh] *na hoíche*.
4. This verb occurs in a variety of forms throughout these texts. Cf. Texts 9, 17, 18, 19, 21 and 22. For the distribution of some of these forms, cf. *LASID* 1, p. 37, 281. Note especially "*Ní* mhuirbhfidhear *choíche mise*" in Text 19 and the remarks in *IDPP*, 221-2 concerning such forms. For the distribution of this kind of future ending, cf. *LASID* 1, p. 192-3 (*pósfaidhear, cuirfidhear*), 282 (*báidhfidhear*). Cf. also *GTh* § 260.
5. *Capall* means " mare " in this dialect (cf. " *leis an chapall* a searrach below and " *bhí sí ag cur* a *cinn* " [Text 7]). *Beathach* (Text 10) is the word for " horse." For the distribution of such words in Ireland, cf. *LASID* 1, p. 52 and for Scotland and Ireland, *CCUS* § 21.8.

6. The personal pronoun *sí* and, as here, the feminine possessive pronoun *a*, are used when referring to this masculine noun.

7. The form *cuir* [-ïr′] is the one most favoured by this speaker. It occurs in Texts 4, 5, 7, 13, 16 and 22; *cur* [-ǫr] occurs in Texts 4, 8, 11, 12, and 22. Both forms are noted in *DD*—" ' to put ' is either [kǫr] or [kyr′] " (56). Cf. *LASID* 4, p. 290, Note 3.

8. *Chuaigh* is pronounced with initial *f-* throughout these texts. For the development of [χ] > [f], cf. *DD* § 313.

4

Colm Cille agus Ár Slánaitheoir

1. For [sõ:ruw / so:nruw], cf. *DD* § 443 and *GTh* §§ 72-3.

5

Colm Cille agus na Bradáin a leag é

1. The verb " *Tá* " as used here in response to a question has the meaning of the English word " well ", which, borrowed and used at the end of a sentence, has the meaning " indeed "—cf. Text 15.

2. The pronunciation of *trasna* as [t′r′asNə], here and below, as well as in Text 22, has not been noted elsewhere in Ulster. Máire Uí Cheallaigh, a native of the Croaghs (cf. p. 84, 85), informs me that the initial *t* of *trasna* is also palatalized in the expression [kləi t′r′asNə] *claí trasna* "a cross-ditch ".

3. *Loch* can be both masculine and feminine. Cf. *GTh* § 489.

6

Tairngreacht Cholm Cille

1. For the absence of the svarabhakti vowel between *r* and *g* and the absence of nasal quality in this word, cf. *DD* §§ 138b, 303.

2. Cf. *LASID* 4, p. 290, Note 6, where it is stated that this typically Donegal expression is also found in Argyllshire.

3. For examples of the double article and its usage, cf. Séamus Ó Searcaigh, " Some uses and omissions of the article in Irish," *The Journal of Celtic Studies* 1 (1950), 239-48. Cf. also *sub* " *in* ", *DIL* I, Fasciculus 2, p. 188. The genitive form " *na hÉireanna* " is widely used in Donegal by older Irish speakers (cf. *IDPP*, 214). Cf. also *LASID* 4, p. 144 (*sub* " *Éire* ") and p. 136, No. 350 (Point 83) as also *GTh* § 445Bb for central and south-west Donegal examples and *IR*, 256, 326 and *IT*, 183 for examples from the north of the county.

7

Bás Cholm Cille

1. Pronounced [sǫlmə] here, but [sǫlə] is also used. Cf. Text 18. For the distribution of these forms, cf. *LASID* 1, p. 121.
2. [kõ:rə] (cf. Text 8) and [kõ:ri:] are used side by side with [kõ:nər']. *Cónair* and *comhra* occur in the following sequence in another version of this story taken down from this speaker—" *Agus bhí a ainm uirthi, ar an* chomhra— *bhí a ainm ar an* chónair . . . *agus* stripáileadh suas an chónair ansin..." (Tape 85/1 SÓC [26.12.1973]). *DD* § 442 only notes [kõ:nir'], deriving it by metathesis from *comhrainn*, an inflected form of *comhra* "a chest". For the distribution of these forms, cf. *LASID* 1, p. 193 and for further references and a discussion of the various Irish and Scottish forms, cf. *CCUS* § 1.7. Cf. also *IDPP*, 241.

8

Cónair Cholm Cille

1. This English loan-word also occurs in Text 16 (" lot *eallaigh* ") and Text 17 (" lot *lánúineach* "). It is also noted in *LASID* 4, p. 143, *sub* " *bean* " (Point 83) " [Lɔt banʰ] ' a crowd of women.' "
2. Other examples of non-lenition occur in Text 9 (" *ar gearria* "), Text 15 (" *ar cloich* "), Text 20 (" *ar téad* ") and Text 21 (" *ar carraig* "). Cf. also *LASID* 4, p. 143, *sub* " *cathaoir* " (Point 83). *IR* § 15 lists many other examples.
3. The English word " bit " is used in phrases such as " bit *ar bith* " (here and twice below) and " *aon* bʰit " (Text 18). Cf. [ɛn v'ït:] " at all," *LASID* 4, p. 143, *sub* " bit " (Point 83). For the use of *giota*—borrowed from English "jot" according to *DD* § 434—cf. Text 12 (" *d'imigh an fhideal ina* giotaí "), Text 15 (" *fá ghiota* díthi ") and Text 21 (" *amach* giota *san fharraige* ").
4. The forms [ɛr'ə ɣɛn'əv'], [nsə ɣɛn'əv'] and [əsə ɣɛn'əv'], all of which occur in this text would seem to reflect the form [gɛn'ẽv] noted in *DD* § 121. The forms [gɛnəv] and [gən'əv'] are noted in *IR* § 771 and *IU* § 103 respectively, but *LASID* 4, p. 142, No. 1076 (Point 83) has [gɛn'uʷ]. Cf. " *a chuid talaimh féin* " [-taləv'] (Text 14) and " farm *maith talaimh* " [-tɔləv'] (Text 18).
5. The disyllabic pronunciation of *lí* [L'i:jə] contrasts with the monosyllabic *luí* [Löi] (Text 17) and in doing so agrees with *DD* §§ 165, 145 [L'iə] and [Lɔi, Ly:]. In north Donegal, the situation is mixed (cf. *DT* §§ 213, 256; *IT*, 295, 297 and *IR*, 275, 276) whereas south-west Donegal only has disyllabic forms (*GTh* §§ 329, 331 [L'i:ə] and [Li:ə (Lɔijə)] (cf. also *GTh* § 545.32). *LASID* 4, p. 140, No. 873 (Point 83) gives [L'i:ə] for *lí* and *ibid.*, p. 135, No. 132 (Point 83), [Lᵊi] for *luí*. For the distribution of the latter, cf. *LASID* 1, p. 148 (Point 83 = [Löi, Lɪ:]). Cf. Note 5, Text 9.
6. *DD* §§ 121, 180 lists both [m'i: hi:n'] and [m'ɛ hein'], a situation reflected in *LASID* 1, p. 297 where the distribution of " *muid féin/sinn féin* " is dealt with. In *CCUS* § 13.6, p. 141-3, the Irish and Scottish distribution of *féin*

is treated with examples given from many different sources and areas. Nearly all the examples that occur in these texts have [i:], showing a raised vowel, but the original vowel may be heard in [ɛ: heːn′ ǫgǝs i: hiːn′] (Text 15).

7. *DD* § 392 quotel [kyN′aL′t′] " to keep " as an example of a parasitic [t′] being added to certain words (those ending in [l′, n′, ʃ]). *Coinneáilt* occurs again in Text 11, but *coinneáil* also occurs in Text 20. *Tógáilt* occurs in Text 18.

8. *Thá* for *tá* occurs three times in these texts—here, in Text 16 and in Text 20. *CCUS* § 12.6, p. 133-4, notes occasional north Donegal occurrences, concluding that they " may be reasonably understood as related directly to the Scottish form (tha) " and noting that " it seems quite likely that *thá* may be known as an alternative form for *tá* in other N. Donegal dialects, even though it has not been recorded from them in A4 (= *LASID* 4)." Cf. also Note 1, Text 15.

9. Cf. *IDPP*, 228-9 where it is stated—" In Northern Irish (and sometimes in Scottish *féin* " self " requires (possibly on the English model) a pronoun to be used between it and the noun it qualifies. . . ."

9

Cailleach Ghallda ina gearria

1. Cf. *GTh* § 415b where the forms [k′er′ǝ wɔ: (bahǝ)] are given.

2. *Gnóthú*, the form used here and below, and the form *gnóthan* have both been noted in *DD* §§ 94, 183, 190 and in *GTh* § 325.

3. Other forms of this verb occur in Text 18.

4. *Rá* and *ráit* are used, side by side (cf. Text 14, where they occur in the same sentence). Cf. *DD* §§ 27, 392 and for the distribution of these forms *LASID* 1, p. 206.

5. *LASID* 4, p. 143 (Point 83) gives a similar monosyllabic diphthongised form. *GTh* § 222 notes both [kliǝ] and [klǝijǝ], while *DD* § 165 only has [kliǝ]. Cf. Note 8, Text 8. Note the strong nasalization, a feature of this speaker's pronunciation.

6. The form *coill* (as opposed to *coillidh* or *coille*) occurs again in Text 19 where the genitive singular form [kïL′uw] also occurs. For the distribution of these forms, cf. *LASID* 1, p. 248 and *CCUS* §§ 5b, 13.4 and 19.1.

7. *Faire* and *tórramh* are the Ulster words for " wake " and " funeral " respectively. For the distribution of these words (and also *sochraid*), cf. *LASID* 1, p. 196.

8. *IR* § 485c also has the verbal noun form *rann*. *IT*, 312 gives [raNt]. Text 18 has the form " *rann mé.* "

9. I have also noted *uisce beatha* from this speaker. Cf. *uisce beatha* (*IT*, 337) and *uisce beatha/uisce bheatha* (*CSTI*, 109).

10. In this text, *cú* is treated as both masculine (" *cú maith dubh* "/" *an cú* ") and and feminine ("*fána muinéal* "). In Erris, Co. Mayo, I have heard " *Cú maith dubh! Is í agus an choin atá ann!*" In *DIL*, C, Fasciculus 3, p. 565, this word is described as " n.m., later also f." and it is also stated that *cú* sometimes appears " with unexplained lenition of a closely following word."

11. This word survives into Hiberno-English as " pishrogues " (cp. *EDD*, 213). Other Irish and Hiberno-English dialect forms include East Ulster *piostrógaí*/ " pistrugs," Connacht *pistreogaí*/" pistrogues " and Munster *piseoga*/" pishogues."

10

"*Come all to me! Come all to me!*"

1. Note the pronunciation [ʃeːn] for " chain " and the inflected form " *ag tarraingt an t*-chain " [t'ʃeːn']. For a discussion of the treatment of English loan-words in Irish and Scottish Gaelic cf. S. Watson, " Loan-words and initial mutations in a Gaelic dialect", *Scottish Gaelic Studies* 14, 1 (1983), p. 100-13. For further examples of inflected loan-words, cf. Texts 3, 6, 12, 13, 17, 18 and 19.

2. *Bealach mór*—not *bóthar* is the normal Donegal usage. Cf. Texts 6 and 14 for further examples. For the distribution of *bealach mór* and *bóthar*, cf. *LASID* 1, p. 80.

3. For this usage, cf. *IDPP*, 288 and *DD* § 454. A further example (" *deoch bhainne* ") occurs in Text 16.

11

An Maistreadh Mór

1. The dative form preserved here also occurs twice below. *Fidil* (Text 12) *cruaich* (Text 15), *sráideoig* (Text 18), *eiteoig* and *glúin* (Text 19) and *muic* (Text 21) provide further examples.

2. Cf. *DD* §§ 253, 452 and for [ə N'iv']—several examples of which occur in Text 19—cf. *DD*, 210.

3. Other forms of this verb (as well as the alternative formation *thúsaigh*) occur in Texts 15, 16, 18 and 22.

4. Pronounced here with what *DD* § 386 calls a "parasitic *t* ". Further examples occur in Texts 18, 19, 21 and 22. [fɑ x'ǫN tǫməL't'] occurs in Text 18, (cp. [ər føg tǫMIL't], *LASID* 4, p. 141, No. 1041 [Point 83]. Cf. Note 5, Text 8; Note 7, Text 8.

5. *DD* § 10 and *LASID* 4, p. 137, No. 486 (Point 83) also give this form.

6. This is unclear.

I

13

An Sagart agus Na Síogaí

1. Here and in Text 14 pronounced [rĭm'ə]. *DD* § 298 notes this and other examples of what is called there the development " of *m* out of *v* " and describes this as being a widespread feature absent, however, " in the speech of any of the younger generation ". For a discussion of palatal -bh-, -mh-, in Irish, cf. *IDPP*, 24-6 and K. Jackson, " Palatalisation of Labials in the Gaelic Languages," *Beiträge zur Indogermanistik und Keltologie, Julius Pokorny zum* 80. *Geburtstag gewidmet* (Innsbrucker Beiträge zür Kulturwissenschaft, Vol. 13, Innsbruck, Ed. Wolfgang Meid).
2. For the use of *ina* (instead of *i n-*) in Ulster Irish, cf. *LASID* 4, p. 284. Note 10; p. 293, Note 3; p. 296, Note 5 and *CCUS* § 21.18.

14

Conall agus na Daoine Beaga

1. The use, as here, of what appears to be a Scottish Gaelic personal pronoun (*e, i, iad* for *sé, sí, siad*) is a subject given comprehensive coverage in *CCUS* § 20.16. Further examples are noted in *IR* § 64, *IU*, 107 and *CSTI*, 154. *LASID* 4, p. 145, *sub* "*ólta*" (Point 83) records the form *e* in [tǫ ə kɔ hɔ :lta l'ɛ hɛl'] Texts 15, 16 and 22 contain further examples.
2. [ə xǫ tɑləv' hi:n'] and again [farə'maix' tɔləv'] (Text 18) contrast with *LASID* 4, p. 141, No. 961 (Point 83) which gives [tɔlu] gsg. [n tɑlu]. Cf. also *IT*, 330 [tɑlu, tɑlə] gsg. [tɑli, tɑlunə]; *IU*, 126 [tɔlü, p'isə tɔlü] and *CSTI*, 105 [tɔlu, tuxɔ'tɔlu] (*do chuid talaimh*). Cf. Note 3, Text 8.
3. The verb " dant " in the meaning " to be afraid " is given in the *Scottish National Dictionary*, Vol. 3 (Edinburgh 1952).

15

An Fear a phós an Mhaighdean Mhara

1. The speaker, echoing my lapse from Ulster usage, says *léithi*, instead of the usual *uirthi*. The preposition " on " is also widely used in Ulster English in association with the verb " to marry "; " married on " = " married to " (cf. *EDD*, 188).
2. For the lenition of *seisear* in this situation, cf. *DD* § 451, Note 1.
3. *Seanduine* means " old man ", the reference, in this instance, being to the speaker's father, Eoghan Phádraig Mac an Luain (cf. p. xxiii).
4. *Ba ea* is here realized as [bǫ γa]. *DD* § 190 gives the form [bə 'ja]. For a discussion of *dh, gh,* cf. *GTh* § 118 and *DD* § 170. Cf. also *adhradh* below and *bleaghan* (Text 18).

16

An Siosanach

1. Cf. *LASID* 4, p. 138, No. 757 (Point 83) [ṛ f′øg] and Note 4, Text 15. It occurs again in Text 19.
2. Subjunctive forms such as these are commonly used in this dialect. A further example (" *go dtige* ") occurs below and other examples occur elsewhere in these texts.
3. Pronounced [ʃïr] by analogy with *siar* [ʃiər]. Cf. *DD* § 89. Cf. [ə′N′ïr] anoir (aniar) in Text 19.
4. Pronounced here and elsewhere in these texts [rö̤:i]. For a description of the vowel sound [ö], cf. *DD* §§ 69-73, 156. For "*réidh*", however, *DD* §§ 95, 271 quotes [rei], [rəi] and [rɛi]. *LASID* 4, p. 141, No. 1020, and *sub* " *réidh*," p. 145 (both Point 83) gives [rö̤:i]. *CSTI*. 144, 182 also gives [rö̤:i]. For the distribution of this sound as it occurs in the word *rogha*, cf. *LASID* 1, p. 23. Other examples of this sound occurring in these texts include " *Lá Thadhg na dTadhgann* " [La: hö̤:g Nə dö̤:gəN] below (cf. *DD* § 426 for [tö̤:g]) and " *aghaidh* " [ö̤:i] in Text 19. Two further examples with *réidh* occur in Texts 18 and 20.

17

Clainn tSuibhne na Miodóg

1. The nominative form " *gruag* ", as opposed to *gruaig*, which is sometimes substituted for it, is used here and in Text 21; in Text 22, in " *i ngruag* ", it actually replaces the dative form *gruaig*. *IU*, 106 also gives [grü:ɑg grühɑg]; *CSTI*, 84 has [gruəg / grʌ̃əg] and *DD* § 270 [gruəg]. *LASID* 4, p. 137, Nos. 376, 378, 381 (Point 83) gives [gru:əG], [mə ɣruəg′] (acc.) and [mǫ ɣru:əg] (acc.).
2. Pronounced [ʃk′ïn′h ?]. Cf. *LASID* 1, p. 165 for the pronunciation of this word in various Irish dialects.

18

An Fear Mór

1. For the distribution of the various dialect words for " potatoes ", cf. *LASID* 1, p. 180.
2. *Recte* " *á ndéanamh* ".
3. Other Donegal forms include *léimnigh* and *léimtrigh*.
4. *Recte* " *ag an Fhear Mhór*."
5. Cf. *LASID* 4, p. 141, No. 960 (Point 83) [f′èr′əm′].
6. For the distribution of the various dialect words for "tongs ", cf. *LASID* 1, p. 166.

7. Cf. *DD* § 21 [g′arwãi] " pretty good " and § 218 [g′ar ˋLa:d′ir′] " middling strong ".
8. For the distribution of this and other verbal noun forms of this verb in the various Irish dialects, cf. *LASID* 1, p. 19.
9. DD § 179 gives [hanəf′æn′]and § 107 [hïnaf′aen′], declaring the latter to be "only one of several pronunciations of the word". *CCUS* § 13.7, p. 142-3 and *IR*, 242 agree with this speaker on the quality of the final vowel. Cf. *LASID* 4, p. 141, No. 1035 (Point 83) [hèN′əf′in′].

19

An Crochaire Tarnocht

1. Cf. Note 1, Text 16.
2. These words are unclear but their general import is readily understood. Seán Ó hEochaidh in his transcription of the 1948 version of this story told by Seán Mac an Bháird (cf. p. xxxiv) writes " *Dara boiste le b*   " (IFC 1949: 45) and " *Dara boiste le briathar* " (IFC 1949: 46). The phrase does not occur in his 1947 transcription (from a recording which does not survive) of the same story from the same informant.
3. In Text 18, the English word " finish " (in " *cuirfidh mise* finish *anocht air* " is substituted for *deireadh*. For examples of the varied usage of *deireadh*, cf. " *similéir agus deireadh* " and " *deireadh a bheith druidte aige* " (Text 11); " *siar deireadh na hoíche* " and " *bhí deireadh thart* " (Text 18); " *chaith sí uaithi deireadh* " (Text 20) and " *dhóigh sé deireadh na mban* " (Text 21).
4. *Neoin* here and again below is treated as a masculine noun. For the development of palatal *n* in this word by " dilation ", cf. *DT* § 504.
5. For a discussion of the forms *pill/till* in Ulster and Scotland, cf. *CCUS* §§ 8.f., 21.21 and for *tilleadh/pilleadh/filleadh*, cf. *LASID* 1, p. 278.
6. Cf. Note 2, Text 11 and *LASID* 1, p. 45. Other examples occur below.
7. Cf. *EDD*, 144. This English loan-word occurs again in Text 20.

20

An Toirtín Beag agus An Toirtín Mór

1. For various dialect forms of this word, cf. *LASID* 1, p. 168.

21

Goll Mac Morna

1. This pronunciation accords with *DD*, 218 and *GTh*, 288, but contrasts with [Nə f′iənu] *IT*, 279 and [Na f′iaNuw] *DT*, 174 (where the form [f′iaNəv] is also listed). IE § 388 gives an ending in / -iv/ for " Fianaibh ".

2. *IE* §§ 7, 10 and 15 provides numerous examples of situations where initial *f* resists lenition. A further example, involving an English loan-word—" Forestry "—occurs in Text 6. Cf. Note 1, Text 10.
3. The form [Nỹ: Nọnuːr'] is found in *DD* § 232 and the development of this pronunciation is discussed in *DD* §§ 59, 105.

22

An Fearghamhain

1. For the distribution of dialect forms of this word, cf. *LASID* 1, p. 32.
2. This is unclear.
3. This is unclear.
4. In his confusion, the storyteller adds a fourth name here. " *Grathaigh* " is later dropped.
5. Pronounced [ʃɛʃan]; cf. [ʃɛhən], Note 1, Text 1. A further example occurs in Text 15. Cf. [L'ɛʃan] (Text 9) and [ɛg'əsan] (Text 10).
6. The *g-* is lenited here, but unlenited later in this sentence. Cf. [fɛd Lɔk'] *IR*, 246; [f'ad 'glɑk'ə] *IT*, 277 and [f'ad ·glak'ə] *DT* § 116.
7. For this development, a further example of which occurs below, cf. *DD* § 470.

INDEX OF TALE TYPES

INDEX OF MIGRATORY LEGENDS

Migratory legend (ML) type numbers refer to *Christiansen* and *Briggs.*

INDEX OF MOTIFS

The references are to Stith Thompson's *Motif-Index of Folk-Literature* (6 vols.: Bloomington, Indiana 1955-1958). Cf. also T. P. Cross, *Motif-Index of Early Irish Literature* (Bloomington, Indiana 1952).

1. Referring to the numbers of the stories.

D1792.	Magic results from curse: 5.
D1810.3.	Magic knowledge from touching "knowledge tooth" with thumb: 21.
D1811.1.1.	Thumb of knowledge: 21.
D1813.3.	"Knowledge tooth" reveals events in distant place: 21.
D1817.3.	Detection of crime through "knowledge tooth": 21.
D1834.	Magic strength from helpful animal: 20.
D1962.2.	Magic sleep by lousing: 20.
D2063.1.1.	Tormenting by sympathetic magic: 11.
D2070.	Bewitching: 20.
D2083.3.	Milk transferred from another's cow by magic: 9, 10.
cf. D2083.3.2.	Witch transfers milk from another's cows by use of hair rope: 10.
D2084.2.	Butter magically kept from coming: 11.
D2085.1.	Curse (by saint) makes river (lake) barren of fish: 5.
D2156.2.	Miraculous increasing of milk from one cow: 8.
D2178.4.	Animals created by magic: 4.
cf. D2157.2.2.	Saint causes wheat to ripen prematurely: 4.

E.   THE DEAD

E710.	External soul: 19.
E711.1.	Soul in egg: 19.
E713.	Soul hidden in a series of coverings: 19.
E765.	Life dependent on external object or event: 19.

F.   MARVELS

F200.	Fairies: 12,13,14.
F230.	Appearances of fairies: 14.
F231.1.6.	Fairy in green clothes: 14.
F236.1.	Color of fairy's clothes: 14.
F236.	Dress of fairies: 14.
F251.	Origin of fairies: 13.
F251.6.	Fairies as fallen angels: 13.
F251.11.	Fairies are people not good enough for heaven but not bad enough for hell: 13.
F253.	Extraordinary powers of fairies: 12.
F262.	Fairies make music: 12.
cf. F262.2.	Fairies teach bagpipe-playing: 12.
F340.	Gifts from fairies: 12.
F343.	Other presents from fairies: 12.
F345.	Fairies mistrust mortals.
F349.	Fairy adviser: 12.
F.531.	Giant: 19.
F.531.1.6.3.1.	Giant (giantess) with particularly long hair: 21.
F531.2.1.	Extremely tall giant: 19.
F531.5.7.	Giants marry human beings: 19.

F852.   Extraordinary coffin: 8.
F863.   Extraordinary chain: 10.
F962.10.   Extraordinary mist (darkness): 21.

G.   OGRES
G84.   Fee-fi-fo-fum: 19.
G204.   Girl in service of witch: 20.
G211.2.7.   Witch in form of hare: 9.
G211.2.7.1.   Witch as hare allows self to be coursed by dogs for pay or for sport: 9.
G257.   Charms to cause witch to reveal herself: 11.
G257.1.   Burning objects forces witch to reveal herself: sympathetic magic: 11.
G265.   Witch abuses property: 9, 10, 11.
G272.   Protection against witches: 9, 11.
G272.2.   Steel powerful against witches: 11.
G272.2.1.   Rowan wood (quicken etc.) protects against witches: 9.
G275.12.   Witch in the form of an animal is injured or killed as a result of the injury to the animal: 9.
G275.13.   Rough treatment of object causes injury or death to witch: 11.
G278.   Death of witch: 9.
G532.   Hero hidden and ogre deceived by his wife (daughter) when he says that he smells human blood: 19.

H.   TESTS
H221.2.   Ordeal by hot iron: 11.
H310.   Suitor tests: 19.
H335.   Tasks assigned suitors: 19.
H900.   Tasks imposed: 19, 20.
H935.   Witch assigns tasks: 20.

J.   THE WISE AND THE FOOLISH
J2541.   "Don't eat too greedily": 18.

K.   DECEPTIONS
K331.   Goods stolen while owner sleeps: 20.
cf. K331.2.1.1. Theft after putting owner to sleep after lousing her: 20.
K525.1.   Substituted object left in bed while intended victim escapes: 18.
K713.1.8.   Women bind warrior's hair to wall of hostel while he sleeps: 21.
cf. K942.   Angry man kills his own horse by mistake: 18.
K955.   Murder by burning: 21.
K956.   Murder by destroying external soul: 19.
K1440.   Dupe's animals destroyed or maimed: 18.
K1840.   Deception by substitution: 18.
K1883.2.   Objects (animals) attacked under the illusion that they are men: 18.

L. REVERSAL OF FORTUNE
L222.   Modest choice: parting gift: 20.

M. ORDAINING THE FUTURE
M205.   Breaking of bargains or promises: 16.
M300-M399.   Prophecies: 1, 6.
M301.5.   Saints (holy men) as prophets: 1, 2, 6.
M363.   Coming of religious leader prophesied: 2.
M364.7.   Coming (birth) of saint prophesied: 2.
M369.   Miscellaneous prophecies: 6.
M391.   Fulfillment of prophecy: 6.
M400.   Curses: 5.
M411.1.   Curse by parent: 20.
M411.8.   Saint's (prophet's) curse: 5.
M476.   Curse on river: 5.
M476.1.   Curse on river or sea: no fish in it from that day: 5.

N. CHANCE AND FATE
N815.   Fairy as helper: 12.
N101.   Inexorable fate: 13, 22.
N440.   Valuable secrets learned: 20.
N800.   Helpers: 20.

Q. REWARDS AND PUNISHMENTS
Q2.   Kind and unkind: 20.
Q10.   Deeds rewarded: 20.
Q40.   Kindness rewarded: 20.
Q51.   Kindness to animals rewarded: 20.
Q111.   Riches as reward: 20.
Q200.   Deeds punished: 4, 20.
Q211.   Murder punished: 21.
Q212.   Theft punished: 20.
Q212.1.   Theft from dwarf (witch) revenged: 20.
Q431.   Punishment: banishment (exile): 3, 21.
Q276.   Stinginess punished: 4.
Q286.   Uncharitableness punished: 4.
Q286.1.   Uncharitableness to holy person punished: 4.
Q292.1.   Inhospitality to saint (god) punished: 4.
Q414.   Punishment: burning alive: 21.
Q551.3.4.   Transformation to stone as punishment: 20.

R. CAPTIVES AND FUGITIVES
R43.   Captivity on island: 21.

S. UNNATURAL CRUELTY
S112.	Burning to death: 21.
S112.0.2.	House (hostel) burned with all inside: 21.
S145.	Abandonment on an island (Marooning): 21.

T. SEX
T68.	Princess offered as prize: 19.
T161.	Jus primae noctis: 17.

V. RELIGION
V70.1.1.	Festival of Beltane (= May Day): 10.
V140.2.	Saint's relics miraculously recovered: 8.
V140.3.	A cow licks the stone under which the secreted body of saint is buried: 8.
V220.	Saints: 1-8.
V211.	Christ: 4.
V211.2.1.2.	Christ disguised as beggar: 4.
V236.1.	Fallen angels become fairies (dwarfs, trolls): 13.
V315.1.	Power of repentance: 4.
cf. V411.6.	Food given away by saint miraculously restored.
V420.	Reward of the uncharitable: 4.
V520.	Salvation: 13.

W. TRAITS OF CHARACTER
W27.	Gratitude: 20.
W152.	Stinginess: 4.
W153.	Miserliness: 4.

Z. MISCELLANEOUS GROUPS OF MOTIFS
Z71.	Formulistic numbers: 17, 19, 21.
Z71.6.	Formulistic number: nine (99, 900, 999, 99,999): 17, 19, 21.

SELECT BIBLIOGRAPHY

AARNE, Antti and THOMPSON, Stith, *The Types of the Folktale,* Second Revision (FF Communications 184 [Helsinki 1961]).

BÉALOIDEAS, *The Journal of the Folklore of Ireland Society,* 1 ff. (1927 ff.).

BRIGGS, Katharine M., *A Dictionary of British Folk-Tales,* 1-4 (London 1970-1) = *Briggs.*

CHRISTIANSEN, Reidar Th., *The Migratory Legends* (FF Communications 175 [Helsinki 1958]) = *Christiansen* and *ML.*

Contributions to a Dictionary of the Irish Language (Dublin 1913-68) = *DIL.*

DINNEEN, Patrick S., *Foclóir Gaedhilge agus Béarla* (Dublin 1927).

EVANS, Emrys, 'The Irish Dialect of Urris, Inishowen, Co. Donegal' (*Lochlann,* Vol. 4 [1969], p. 1-130) = *IU.*

HAMILTON, John N., *The Irish of Tory Island* (Studies in Irish Language and Literature, Department of Celtic, Q.U.B., 3, [Belfast 1974]) = *IT.*

HENEBRY, Richard and KELLEHER, Andrew, *Betha Colaim Cille* (*Zeitschrift für celtische Philologie* 3 [1901], p. 516-71; 4 [1903], p. 276-331; 5 [1905], p. 26-87; 9 [1913], p. 242-87; 10 [1915], p. 228-65) = *BCC (ZCP).*

HOLMER, Nils M., *The Irish Language in Rathlin Island, Co. Antrim* (RIA, Todd Lecture Series, Vol. 18 [Dublin 1942]) = *IRI.*

HUYSHE, Wentworth (Trans.), *The Life of Saint Columba* (London 1905) = *VSC.*

KENNEY, James F., *The Sources for the Early History of Ireland* (Dublin 1979).

LAOIDE, Seosamh, *Cruach Chonaill* (Dublin 1913) = *CC.*

LUCAS, L. W., *Grammar of Ros Goill Irish, Co. Donegal* (Studies in Irish Language and Literature, Department of Celtic, Q.U.B., 5, [Belfast 1979]) = *IR.*

MAC RÓIGH, Feargus (= Énrí Ó Muirgheasa), *Maighdean an tSoluis agus Scéalta Eile* (Dundalk 1913) = *MS.*

— *Oidhche Áirneáil i dTír Chonaill* (Dundalk 1925) = *OA.*

MHAC AN FHAILIGH, Éamonn, *The Irish of Erris, Co. Mayo* (Dublin 1968) = *IE.*

Ó BAOILL, Colm, *Contributions to a Comparative Study of Ulster Irish and Scottish Gaelic* (Studies in Irish Language and Literature, Department of Celtic, Q.U.B., 4 [Belfast 1978]) = *CCUS.*

Ó CATHÁIN, Séamas, *The Bedside Book of Irish Folklore* (Dublin and Cork 1980) = *BBIF.*

— Irish Life and Lore (Dublin and Cork 1982) = *ILL.*

Ó CRÓINÍN, Seán and Ó CRÓINÍN, Donncha, *Seanachas Amhlaoibh Í Luínse* (Folklore Studies 5 [Dublin 1980]) = *SAIL.*

Ó DÓNAILL, Niall, *Foclóir Gaeilge-Béarla* (Baile Átha Cliath 1977).

Ó Duilearga, Séamus, *Leabhar Sheáin Í Chonaill* (Baile Átha Cliath 1948) = *LSIC*.

Ó hEochaidh, Seán, "Colm Cille sa tSeanchas", *Irisleabhar Muighe Nuadhat* 1963, p. 33-50 = *IMN*.

Ó hEochaidh, Seán and Wagner, Heinrich, "Sean-Chainnt na gCruach", *Zeitschrift für celtische Philologie*, Vol. 29 (1962-4), p. 1-90 = *SCC*.

Ó hEochaidh, Seán, Ní Néill, Máire and Ó Catháin, Séamas, *Síscéalta ó Thír Chonaill/Fairy Legends from Donegal* (Folklore Studies 4 [Dublin 1977]) = *SS*.

O'Kane, James, "Placenames of Inniskeel and Kilteevoge", *Zeitschrift für celtische Philologie*, Vol. 31 (1970), p. 59-145 = *PIK*.

O'Kearney, Nicholas, *The Prophecies of Saints Colum-cille, Maeltamlacht, Ultan, Senan, Bearcan, and Malachy* (Dublin 1932 [reprint of 1856 ed.]) = *NOK*.

O'Kelleher, A. and Schoepperle, G., *Betha Colaim Cille/Life of St. Columcille* (University of Illinois Bulletin, Vol. 15, No. 48 [Urbana, Ill., 1918]) = *BCC (OKS)*.

O'Rahilly, Thomas, *Irish Dialects Past and Present* (Dublin 1932) = *IDD*.

Ó Súilleabháin, Seán, *A Handbook of Irish Folklore* (Dublin 1942).

— and Christiansen, Reidar Th., *The Types of the Irish Folktale* (FF Communications 188 [Helsinki 1967]) = *TIF*.

O'Sullivan, Seán, *Legends from Ireland* (London 1977) = *LI*.

Ó Tuathail, Éamonn, *Sgéalta Mhuintir Luinigh* (Dublin 1933) = *SML*.

Otway, Caesar, *Sketches in Ireland descriptive of interesting and hitherto unnoticed districts in the North and South* (Dublin 1827).

Quiggin, E. C., *A Dialect of Donegal* (Cambridge 1906) = *DD*.

Skene, W. F., "The old Irish Life of Colum-cille", *Celtic Scotland*, Vol. 2 (Edinburgh 1877), p. 467-507 = *OIL*.

Sommerfelt, Alf, *The Dialect of Torr, Co. Donegal* (Christiania 1922) = *DT*.

Stockman, Gerard, *The Irish of Achill* (Studies in Irish Language and Literature, Department of Celtic, Q.U.B., 2 [Belfast 1974]) = *IA*.

Stockman, Gerard and Wagner, Heinrich "Contributions to a Study of Tyrone Irish", *Lochlann*, Vol. 3 (1965), p. 43-236 = *CSTI*.

Traynor, Michael, *The English Dialect of Donegal* (Dublin 1953) = *EDD*.

Wagner, Heinrich, *Linguistic Atlas and Survey of Irish Dialects*, Vols. 1 and 4 (Dublin 1958 and 1969) = *LASID*.

— *Gaeilge Theilinn* (Dublin 1959) = *GTh*.

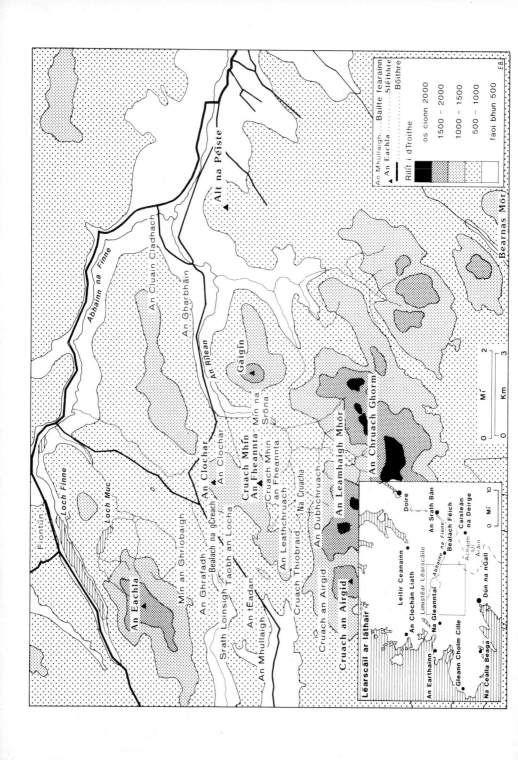

Léarscáil ar láthair

Limistéar Léarscáile

Leitir Ceanainn

An Clochán Liath

An Earthainn

Na Gleanntaí

Gleann Choilm Cille

Abhainn na Finne

Bealach Féich

Caisleán na Deirge

Achadh na nGall

Aráin

Dún na nGall

Na Cealla Beaga

Doire

An Srath Bán

An Mhullaigh .... Bailte fearainn
An Eachla .... Sléibhte
.... Bóithre

Rílíf i dTroithe

os cionn 2000
1500 – 2000
1000 – 1500
500 – 1000
faoi bhun 500

Rílíf i dTroithe

Bearnas Mór

Alt na Péiste

Abhainn na Finne

An Cluain Cladhach

An Gharbhán

An Ríleán

Gáigín

Cruach Mhín
An Fheannta

Cruach Mhín
an Fheannta

Mín na
Sróna

An Leathchruach

Cruach Thíobraid

Na Cruacha

An Dubhchruach

An Leamhaigh Mhór

An Chruach Ghorm

Cruach an Airgid

Cruach an Airgid

An Clochar
An Clochar

Bealach na gCreach

An Ghrafadh

Srath Loinsigh

Taobh an Locha

An tÉadan

An Mhullaigh

Mín an Ghríobaigh

An Eachla

Loch Muc

Loch Finne

Fíontún

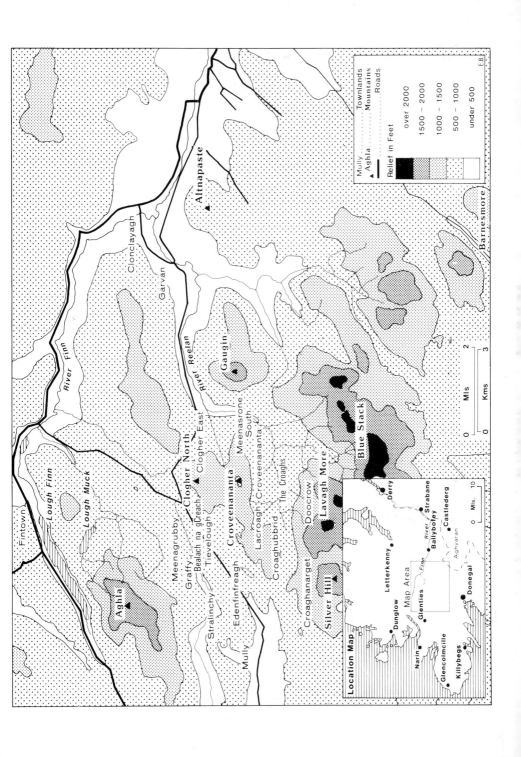

Location Map

Relief in Feet

over 2000
1500 – 2000
1000 – 1500
500 – 1000
under 500

Mully .... Townlands
Aghla ▲ Mountains
Roads

Fintown

Lough Finn

River Finn

Lough Muck

Aghla ▲

Meenagrubby

Graffy
Bealach na gCreach
Tievelough
Stralinchy

Edenfinfreagh

Mully

Clogher North
Clogher East

Croveenananta
Lacroagh Croveenananta
South
The Croaghs
Croaghubbrid

Croaghanarget
Doocrow

Silver Hill ▲

Lavagh More

Meenasrone

Gaugin ▲

Clonclayagh

Garvan

River Reelan

Altnapaste ▲

Blue Stack

Barnesmore

0   Mls   2
0   Kms   3

Derry
Letterkenny
Strabane
Ballybofey
Castlederg
River Finn
Aghyaran

Dunglow

Glenties
Map Area

Narin
Donegal

Glencolmcille

Killybegs

0   Mls   10

E.B.